CONSUMERISM

It was March, 1962, when the late President John F. Kennedy spoke of the four basic rights of consumers: the right to be informed, the right to safety, the right to choose and the right to be heard. Since then, a new word has been gaining importance among those responsible for supplying the public with products — *Consumerism.*

Lest you think the producers are the ones establishing the ground rules, and making it a challenge to the consumer to find out what those rules are, here are some quotations on this subject from presidents of very large consumer-product corporations:

"Giving guaranteed quality to the consumer is the most profitable way to be in business."

"We have to stop seeing the consumer as a threat and look upon him as an opportunity."

"Some businesses still don't have the good sense to respond creatively to consumerism. The worst possible way is by window-dressing."

"We should have been involved years ago, all we've been doing is reacting, while consumerism has become the politician's bag."

And many politicians *have* taken advantage of the new movement!

In studying this complex problem, there were times when we felt the subject was insignificant, when you consider the total gripes in the light of a trillion dollar gross national product! Surely the consumer understands economic feasibility as one of the tests? Witness this:

A nationwide (1969) study of consumer attitudes towards food and grocery manufacturers, and their products, indicated only one out of ten expressed an unfavorable opinion.

American Airlines annually receives complaints from only about one-tenth of 1% of its almost nine million passengers.

Good Housekeeping magazine recently polled 1,000 members of its Consumer Panel for their view on the products they buy. The major finding was that 90% of the respondents expressed satisfaction. Only one woman in ten found grounds for complaint!

Nationwide studies show that consumer frustration with government services exceeds by far the gripes against the private enterprises.

While the consumer has many justifiable complaints against the conduct of manufacturers and/or producers, we would like to suggest the consumer has been *his* own worst enemy! There has been a vast "responsibility gap": the consumer has failed to convey his feelings, his reactions to the proper parties, whether it be Government, State or the producer!

The latter is not merely a name, or non-feeling machine producing profit for the stockholders. They know the consumer has to be satisfied, or they aren't going to be in business. But if nobody — or very few — consumers tell the producer, how will he know — except for a slow and long-lasting decline in sales?

Sometimes whole industries are at fault with *their* defense. You've heard: "Thousands of children are poisoned annually because drugs come in containers that are too easily opened." The defense: "Adults should keep dangerous products out of the reach of children."

Or: "The trend to lightweight one-way glass for carbonated beverages has increased the incidence of injuries caused by bursting bottles." Defense: "If you compare the annual number of bottles filled with the injury rate, the number of accidents are negligible."

When you are left with a big question mark in *your* mind about the contents of a package, when you are concerned about containers, when you are dissatisfied with your purchase, we recommend you, as a *consumer,* bring it to the attention of the clerk or store manager. And, we would suggest a follow-up letter to the president of the company. (Aim high, you'll generally hit your objective).

Don't just boycott the product: sales will drop off and instead of reaching your prime objective of a better product, the manufacturer or producer will merely spend more money for advertising the same, repulsive merchandise!

Extreme measures, such as unlimited class actions, should have no place in the consumer movement: they are primitive, costly to everyone concerned, and are unnecessary, if the proper action is taken by both buyer and seller.

Few consumers today, regardless of how expert they may be in their own profession, have the know-how to buy complex items intelligently, or to select wisely from the wide array of items offered. If the basic strength of consumerism forces the manufacturer (producer) to do a better job of quality control, labeling and packaging, it could be a blessing to everyone.

Our grandmothers may have picked and canned their own foods, knew what they were feeding their families, but today's market shopper almost has to be a chemist to know what she's buying!

For example the instructions on a popular children's drink read, in part: "Pour contents into large, non-metal pitcher." A thinking mother has to ask herself, "What does it do to metal? What will it do to my child's stomach?" (The drink contains citric acid, which is non-compatible with metal.)

Would you give a child a product of fumaric acid, sugar, monosodium phosphate, vitamin C, propylane glycal, artificial color, calcium carbonate, dioctyl sodium sulfosuccinate? Believe it or not, these are the contents of a powdered drink (to be mixed with water), popular with the very young.

While labeling of the contents of a package, such as the above examples, are mandatory in today's marketing of products, the consumer depends in great part upon the integrity of the merchant, the manufacturer and the constant policing of the latter's activities by various Federal agencies.

And have you noticed they are putting more food in with your additives lately? We are confident, in the not-too-distant future, the manufacturer (and/or producer) will also be required to explain to the consumer the reasons for each of the products or chemicals in the package.

While the businessman, by the consumer movement, has been made to look like the "bad guy", most companies have, and do, demonstrate a sense of responsibility as a good corporate citizen. But, our own affluence, our more complex way of life, our demand for different products, demand for seemingly better products, tend to *create problems of understanding!*

Unfortunately, the people who have been exploited the most by the rascals of all industry have been the all-too-large group of uneducated, or poorly educated, who can ill-afford the 200% interest charges represented by the seller as "only $14.00 a month". Or, who do not understand the door-to-door salesman will not, *can not*, be there if the unknown brand vacuum cleaner fails to work next month. Thus, the problem goes well beyond the simple needs of an informed public.

Our study of consumerism, discussing it with friends, seemed to indicate a grass root frustration on the occasional product that didn't work right — or as long as they thought it should. Who do you contact? To whom do you appeal?

But, let's start at the beginning. An informed consumer will buy from a reliable business man. Don't shop for price alone. Read advertisements carefully. Take contracts seriously. Get all guarantees and warranties in writing and read them carefully. Don't sign any contracts or agreements until you understand fully the contents and mutual obligations.

When former President Kennedy spoke of the four basic rights of consumers, he appointed The Consumer Advisory Counsel, composed of representatives of Government as well as private citizens specially qualified to represent the consumer. The Chairman of the Committee is the Special Assistant to the President for Consumer Affairs.

The Committee welcomes recommendations, suggestions of interest to consumers. A soft-cover book titled, "A Guide to Federal Consumer Services", is available, giving information about forty agencies, or divisions of agencies, of the U.S. government, with an intended purpose to provide basic information on current Federal consumer-protection programs.

If these programs are to produce the full benefit intended, the consumer must know *what* they are and how they can be used. Over the years, the activities of the Federal government have grown to the point where nearly every agency performs *some* sort of consumer service, either directly or indirectly.

To volunteer your suggestions, and/or secure the book, write Special Assistant to the President for Consumer Affairs, c/o The White House, Washington, D. C.

Many states and cities have consumer-protection activities widely distributed among a number of agencies. Learn about them in advance — know your rights as a consumer. We would suggest writing The Division of Consumer Affairs at your State capitol. In all likelihood, they will send you a booklet illustrating State laws — but more importantly — should tell you what procedure to follow in your State should you, as a consumer, feel you have been wronged.

Most state and city consumer organizations are associated with the Consumer Federation of America, 1012 14th St., N.W., Washington, D. C. 20005. They can supply names of State and local associations that would be helpful to you, as a consumer, with your specific problem.

If you are not armed in advance on a problem confronting you as a consumer, free counsel and guidance at the local level will be given by the Better Business Bureau, the Chamber of Commerce, the State or County Attorney's office, the Legal Aid Society, the police department — or you may find the company that made the product has a local office.

In shopping for food: Select a reputable food store; make a plan before you do your shopping; read the labels — understand what you're buying; buy according to grade and/or content specifications; buy on nutritive value so your family is properly fed; buy a brand of product you know represents basic quality responsibility, and, seek basic quality rather than deluxe features.

In fresh fruits and vegetables, the consumer selects a raw, unadulterated product produced by nature and man, generally thoroughly washed and, with the exception of many members of the vegetable "family", conveniently ready to use!

But, you say, your young wife wants convenience? Even in vegetables, the fact is that between washing and cooking you can prepare most fresh vegetables in less time than it takes to cook most of the frozen variety, where you boil the water, add the product, second boil and then simmer. With today's quick-steam cookery, fresh is a matter of minutes!

And how much work is it to peel a banana, eat an apple, toss a few berries — or cut crisp vegetables like carrots, celery or peppers? Or, how long does it take to pop a potato in the oven and set the temperature?

This book is a small part of our own involvement in consumerism.

Management has seen too many homemakers thumping watermelons — and not knowing what they were supposed to hear; too many men shoppers picking up green peaches or nectarines — in the belief they'll be ripe by tomorrow; shoppers taking advantage of the red-hot sale on small, green, non-creamy looking honeydews, which, several months later will still be green and apparently immortal.

We firmly believe you should receive a dollar's worth of tasteful, nourishing eating for every dollar you spend in the fresh fruit and vegetable department of your local retail store. Only with this satisfaction will you return. We plan on being in business for many, many years and we would like to convey to you the basics of good selections, the nutritive values, how to handle the product, how to store it — and a few brief suggestions for using the merchandise.

After reading this, we hope you'll enter the fresh fruit and vegetable world with greater confidence — and more frequently!

USING THIS BOOKLET

This fourth, revised edition of the Blue Goose Buying Guide for fresh fruits and vegetables was designed and created with several objectives. Primarily, it is a training-guidance-informational publication on the industry. It should be found valuable to the trainer, produce clerk and student of marketing in the food field.

Uppermost in our mind was the *consumer* of "fresh", who, in general, has been groping her way through produce departments without product knowledge — for much too long a period of time.

To the nutritionist — and we hope everyone is aware of the need for good nutrition — we believe this book creates new information and guidance on the value of fresh fruits and vegetables.

While this book is devoted entirely to fresh fruits and vegetables, "Blue Goose" is also prominent on a complete line of frozen and canned fruits and vegetables, primarily in "institutional-size" units. As with "fresh", every package represents "the best of the better crops".

NUTRITION

There is a new awareness in the world to the need for good nutrition, with the entire food industry in America reversing its negativeness and taking a more positive stance to assist the consumer in securing the vital elements needed by the human body.

The basic stimuli was probably the White House Conference on Food, Nutrition and Health — and out of that came the food industry's National Awareness campaign of the Food Council of America to "Eat the Basic 4 Foods Every Day" — two or more servings daily of the MEAT GROUP; four or more servings daily of the VEGETABLE & FRUIT GROUP; four or more servings daily of the BREADS & CEREALS GROUP, and, daily use of the MILK GROUP.

It was no small contribution to the whole program that the advocates of Organic Foods suddenly added, through national publicity and more effective and extravagant word-of-mouth claims, their own "natural foods" philosophy. "Health Food" stores sprung up like weeds, and the Establishment found that instead of the patrons being "little old ladies in tennis shoes", as popularly believed, crowding the stores for purchases were "average" people! And, admittedly, a predominance of food faddists, hippies and teen-age kids, who were carrying a new "banner". The movement has sparked an overwhelming mass of literature, striking out against the alleged presence of "poisons" in food.

And the shopper in today's retail store is tempted by clever advertising and attractive packaging, bright colors and convenience; and thus, many times paying for things which have no food value, yet which account for a substantial part of the food budget.

(Of every $20 spent for groceries, the consumer is paying close to $2 for the packaging that helps keep the food in good condition and attracts the "buy" attention. Packaging costs vary greatly — the trend is toward smaller packages to meet food needs for single meals, thus reducing waste.)

"Empty calories" — "nutrient poverty" — are becoming common phrases in our vocabulary. But, there is no need — with Nutritional Awareness!

The key to good nutrition is *variety — but with every*

meal! Ironically, this lack of variety is happening at a time when grocery stores are loaded with an enormous choice of different and interesting foods — more than ever before! Most people have the idea (for the reasons previously itemized), that one can eat doughnuts (or nothing) for breakfast-time, pizza for lunch and his diet will contain the needed nutrients — as long as they have the usual meat, potatoes and vegetables for dinner. Not so!

Be adventuresome, avoid the food rut, try foods you don't usually eat! Prepare foods so that you get the most nutrition out of them — it can be done so that even people who are fighting a weight problem can eat a great many different things.

The very simple, but complex, problem in nutrition is that people eat what they like and what they like may be influenced by many factors, including tradition, religion and ceremony; the ways they are accustomed to buying and preparing foods also play important roles.

The consumer, for example, has acquired through the years some unusual ideas about the color of what he eats. White bread is believed purer than brown; in many areas of the country brown eggs are preferred to white, but the color of the shell makes no difference in food value; in many areas, red-skinned potatoes command a premium over white, again without reason.

Since many staple foods are dull-tasting, there is a tendency to look to the frying pan for flavor, to liberal sugaring, condiments or sauces to stimulate the appetite and add interest to the food.

Each day your meals should supply you with
> Protein for growth
> Minerals and vitamins to keep the body
> > functioning properly
> Fats and carbohydrates for energy.

How much of each is your decision, but try to include some in each of your three meals a day. The recommended daily dietary allowances are included in a table at the back of this book.

Here is a simple guide:
> Leafy green vegetables and yellow vegetables for vitamins and minerals.
> Citrus fruits, tomatoes, raw cabbage and salad greens for vitamin C.
> Potatoes, other roots and fruits, for starch, vitamins and minerals.
> Milk and milk products for calcium.
> Meat, poultry, fish, eggs and legumes for protein and minerals.
> Bread, flour and cereals for energy, vitamins, iron and minerals.
> Butter and margarine, or vegetable oil, for vitamin A, among other things.

Some may wonder at the last recommendation. In nutrition studies, responsible agencies are finding a necessity for the diet to include a supply of oil of some kind in the daily diet. It's not butter versus margarine, but saturated fats versus polyunsaturated fats. It can be margarine if it's polyunsaturated — cottonseed oil, corn oil, safflower oil. And, the monounsaturated fats, like olive oil.

Today, the Food & Drug Administration, and the food industry, are working toward development of an informative labeling program for the consumer; and, some food chains are developing an experimental labeling program to advise consumers of vitamin-mineral content in the regular food items in the stores that will be meaningful to the consumer.

The food industry has not failed to produce nourishing foods, but it has failed to educate the public to the best food *choices* — and failed in *identification* of the nourishment, or lack of nourishment, in foods. As a prominent authority on nutritional writings has observed about the food industry today, "The American supermarket is the world's biggest, most complete, most amazing full service nutrient bank."

It is a rather sad commentary in America today that grammar and high schools require courses in economics, so people will understand free enterprise and the capitalistic system; they require courses in civics so they will be good citizens; they require foreign languages, so they will have better world understanding — and yet we all eat three times a day (or oftener), and very little, if any, training is offered in these schools relating to good nutrition, problems of production, distribution and preservation of food!

Our graduates from grammar and high schools know nothing about food additives, nutritional body requirements, the behavior of the elements of nutrition — or the complexities relating to standards of quality.

Surely this will change as the need for Nutritional Awareness becomes more apparent.

Fresh and Natural!

Let us consider the value of fresh fruits and vegetables to good nutrition. First of all, food has to be available — and the U.S. system of good distribution and preservation of fresh product is one of the wonders of the world! It is well-known that the U.S. retail system — one link in the distribution chain — is being copied in many parts of the world. To the U.S. consumer today, it is not unusual for seventy or more distinctly different kinds of fresh produce to be offered in the market simultaneously — and many times this will exceed 100.

Fruits and vegetables are constantly available at

prices the average consumer can readily pay. When malnutrition in our affluent society becomes a problem, it is not for lack of food, but rather a poor *selection* of food.

In this connection, it is interesting to note that more fruits and vegetables, especially in fresh form and without added sugar, starch or fat, can be eaten in relatively large amounts, even in a reducing diet.

Essential *minerals,* which are provided by most fruits and vegetables, include (without suggesting these have special nutritional significance): iodine, magnesium, manganese, phosphorus, potassium, sodium, sulfur, copper, cobalt, zinc, fluorine and molybdenum.

Vitamins not previously named, found in many fruits and vegetables (also without claim of nutritional significance, but only as a matter of interest) are: pyridoxine (vitamin B_6), biotin, pantothenic acid and vitamin E.

Many fruits and vegetables contain pectin, and it has been found that a diet rich in fruits and vegetables tends to reduce the cholesterol level of the blood serum below what it would otherwise be — by a statistically significant amount.

Oral environment is an important factor in tooth health. The carbohydrate most responsible for tooth decay is sugar in all forms, but more especially in forms that stick to the teeth. This emphasizes the need for "detergent foods" as the last food eaten at a meal or snack.

A detergent food is one that sweeps over the teeth and soft tissues, cleansing them of debris. Examples of these foods, as stated by the American Dental Assn., are fruits such as apples and oranges, uncooked vegetables such as carrots and celery. Matter of fact, all raw vegetables, such as lettuce, cabbage, radishes, turnips, raw greens of all kinds, onions and tomatoes; and, all juicy raw fruits such as peaches, plums, apricots, cherries, grapes, melons, pears and citrus, are detergent foods!

Conserving Nutrients

The three R's of cooking to preserve nutrients in fresh fruits and vegetables, as given by associates of the U.S. Department of Agriculture, are: *Reduce* the amount of water used; *Reduce* the length of the cooking period and *Reduce* the amount of surface area exposed.

Also, proper refrigeration and humidity are very important in conserving not only basic product freshness, but also nutrients. (Guidelines for this, each commodity, have been included in this book).

Likewise, proper ripening of fruits is important. (In the case of vegetables, other than tomatoes, ripening is not a factor. Keeping vegetables in covered containers, or film bags, helps to prevent evaporation and

withering).

Use of a tight-fitting pan, when boiling product, is important. Waterless cooking does not permit quick cooking; thus, is no better than cooking vegetables quickly in a small amount of water.

Boiling root or tuber vegetables (carrots, sweet potatoes, potatoes) in their skins retains more vitamins and minerals than cooking after cutting and paring.

Potatoes boiled whole, in their skins, retain practically all their vitamin C, thiamin and other nutrients. Baking tubers whole, in their skin, helps conserve nutritive values.

Panning is a quick way of cooking vegetables in a covered frying pan, helps conserve nutrients in succulent vegetables such as cabbage, summer squash, kale and collards.

Steaming under pressure is quick and satisfactory — if cooking period is carefully timed. Prolonged cooking under pressure results in loss of food value.

Expensive equipment for cooking is not essential.

Holding and re-heating cooked vegetables causes additional loss of nutrients, particularly vitamin C.

Orange juice can be held in the refrigerator for several days before any vitamin C is lost. A lid on the juice container is unimportant.

Berries lose their nutrients quickly after they are capped — or bruised.

Whole citrus fruits keep their nutrients well for several days at room temperature — better and longer when refrigerated.

Fresh oranges lose nutritive value if they are strained. The edible yield of strained orange juice is only two-thirds to three-fourths that of the orange eaten by sections.

Eat the basic 4 foods every day.

ORGANIC FOODS

There are many different definitions for organically-grown foods. All revolve around "nature" or "naturalness". Simply, not man-made. Fresh fruits and vegetables, for example, cannot be grown with the use of chemical fertilizers, soil conditioners, insecticides or any such type of spray, pesticide or preservative; and, the ground used must have been dormant for at least three years — or proven to be free of chemical fertilizers or residues from previously-used pesticides or herbicides — before it can be said, "This is organically-produced food."

But, no *absolute* definition or guideline exists. Fertilizer for plant nutrient comes from humus; humus comes from compost, the latter from nature-produced leaves, twigs, grass, etc. Healthy plants, or seeds, are prime necessities.

Perhaps the real "father" of the present organic food movement was an Englishman named Sir Albert Howard, who died in 1947. All his personal papers were lost in a fire, but a portion of a popular book says, "(He) was the first to attract attention to diet on a national scale in England, the first to make known to poor people the value of health and hygiene . . . that good food is man's best medicine."

The first extensive documentation of a "chain of health" was made by Sir Albert Howard. Trained as a botanist, he was first employed mainly in the investigation of crop diseases and pests, and in this pursuit, his work took him throughout the world.

In India he observed an area where crops grown were remarkably free from pests; such things as insecticides and fungicides found no place in their ancient system of cultivation. He observed that the key factors were development of healthy strains of plants, and, soil fertility through humus — decomposed and decomposing organic matter.

When Howard retired and returned to England in 1931, he had evolved a complete and revolutionary approach to soil fertility, nutrition and health, which, in effect, is the chain of reasoning behind today's advocates of organically-grown foods:

"1. The birthright of all living things is health.

"2. This law is true for soil, plant, animal and man: the health of these four is one connected chain.

"3. Any weakness or defect in the health of any earlier link in the chain is carried on to the next and succeeding links, until it reaches the last, namely, man.

"4. The widespread vegetable and animal pests and diseases, which are such a bane to modern agriculture, are evidence of a great failure of health in the second (plant) and third (animal) links of the chain.

"5. The impaired health of human populations (the fourth link) in modern civilized countries is a consequence of this failure in the second and third links.

"6. This general failure in the last three links is to be attributed to failure in the first link, the soil: the undernourishment of the soil is at the root of all. The failure to maintain a healthy agriculture has largely cancelled out all the advantages we have gained from our improvements in hygiene, in housing and our medical discoveries."

Our study of the organic food movement reveals the equivalent of volumes of documentation by *individuals* who have proven to themselves, and to many others through their writings, the positive, healthful effects in eating products grown organically.

But, to our knowledge, no generally-accepted, *known* agency anywhere in the world, has *documented* the fact that organically-grown products are more healthful, more nutritious, than what you can purchase in the average retail grocery!

What *is* vastly different in the diet of the organic advocate is *what* he eats and the *variety* — and many of these items cannot be bought at the average corner grocery: a variety of organically-grown fruits and vegetables; corn oil capsules; alfalfa sprouts, soybean sprouts, wheat germ oil capsules, unbleached flour, raw and unpasteurized milk and cream, to name a few. Millet, sunflower seeds and sesame seeds are frequently available at your grocer.

It is curious to note that with all this belief in the benefits of the organically-grown foods, we have yet to find a single advocate who does not take a nutritive supplement, a pill, "naturally compounded" though it might be.

Authors call them "kooks", "food faddists", "natural nuts", "hippies" — or even worse. It impresses us, however, that the organic food "believer" has a *dedication* to health, and intense belief — almost a religion — to the extreme that he has disciplined his mind and body to the ultimate in his own *nutritional program*.

Everyone could use this dedication! Isn't this what Nutritional Awareness is all about?

But let's take a look at what the recognized authorities and agencies say. Dr. Philip L. White, Sc.D., Secretary of the Council on Foods and Nutrition, wrote us, when we asked about the nutritional difference between regular and organically-grown foods:

"While these foods are specially treated or grown in a manner not typical of most of our food supply, an attempt to contrast the organically grown with the more abundant foods in other ways (nutritive value or wholesomeness), will seem to be little more than verbiage until research indicates a basis for such a contrast."

In a syndicated column, F. J. Stare, M.D., Department of Nutrition, Harvard University, was asked by a reader, "Fruits and vegetables in supermarkets are devitalized since they are grown in depleted soil and are sprayed with poisons. How can such fruits and vegetables look and taste so good yet be so inferior to organically-grown products?" The answer: "They are not inferior. The nutritive qualities of fruits and vegetables, also of cereals, are mainly determined by the *genetic composition of the seed*, not by the fertilization of the soil. Fertilization is important in the yield, and in this respect there is no difference between chemical and organic fertilizers applied at the same level of soil nutrients provided."

In a syndicated article, Dr. White again said, "The gist of the matter is that malnutrition caused by inappropriate food choices is blamed on the foods per se rather than on the consumer's food choices, reflecting ignorance or indifference."

As this is written, we learned the U. S. Department of Health, Education and Welfare commissioned a U. of California (Davis) graduate to study the natural health movement and its possible merits; the study is still incomplete. His findings thus far indicate no real advantage to a person selecting organically-grown fruits and vegetables (as an example) over those in regular, commercial production. In an interview, he observed that a few natural health "nutritionists" have university educations, but thus far he has not found one with a degree in nutritional science!

The natural health movement has created its own vocabulary, a tough problem to cope with in itself. They say "purification" means getting closer to nature. To a scientist, "purifying" means getting rid of some of nature's contaminants — as in purifying water.

The natural health movement draws a sharp line in defining "chemical." The scientist makes no distinction between a chemical in the body, of which it is made up, and a chemical formulated in a factory.

To the health food advocate, "organic" foods are grown without synthetic sprays or fertilizers. To the horticulturist, anything which grows, with or without sprays or chemical fertilizers, is organic.

Another handicap is the phrase, "Health Foods." The thinking person knows there is no such thing as "Health Foods". Health is the result of many factors, one of which is food. The body does not require any particular food but uses, in varying amounts, more than 50 nutrients. None of these is a "health" nutrient, but by definition, any nutrient required for human nutrition is essential to life and health, even though some are required in minute amounts.

"The term 'health foods' is a misnomer," says the American Medical Assn.

And, the writers on organic foods have been most clever. One prolific writer headed an article, "Climate is not the Cause of Fertility." The average reader suddenly feels this has been a common point of acceptance throughout the world — and finally an "organic" specialist has exploded the theory! But such is not the case!

Or, "Mrs. Housewife is beginning to realize . . . she's been serving . . . deficient in essential nutrients, heavily laced with sugar and potentially-dangerous chemicals . . ." As for "deficiency", it is so true (Americans seem to specialize in the "nutrient poverty" area!) As to "potentially-dangerous", there is potential danger everywhere, but there is rhetorical dynamite in those words!

"An Alternative to Poisonous Pesticides," is another phrase designed to throw fear in the non-organic believer. The pesticides better be poisonous, or the grower is not going to achieve his objective of producing fine quality, good eating product by preserving it for the date of maturity, instead of letting the many creatures of air and ground prey on the merchandise. His own controls, assiduously policed by Federal and State agencies, gives the consumer assurance none of those pesticides remain for human consumption!

Besides healthy, vigorous plants, the organic people recommend the technique of "biological control" as an alternate to pesticides. This type of control is very possible! It is conceivable to import, or for a grower to "raise" and maintain a supply of ladybugs, preying mantis, or a special wasp that feeds on weevils found in alfalfa, but we seriously doubt it can be done on the mass farming methods employed today, which have assured such a consistent supply of low-cost food. After all, some of these predators are non-compatible and the quiet army of insect defenders could be self-eliminating.

Organic people recommend humus secured from compost piles, instead of the usual well-balanced, man-made fertilizers. A compost pile requires vegetable matter (truly an excellent method of disposing of these wastes), organic kitchen wastes (no meat or fat), and a source of nitrogen. They say, "For a nitrogen source, which is desirable to aid in decomposing the other matter, you can use dog manure, the contents of the cat box, horse manure or steer manure, obtained both cheaply and in small amounts from plant nurseries." Since the humus is then worked into the ground, and what is in the ground goes into the plant, don't you think someone should be concerned about what the dog, the cat, the horse and steer eat first?

While it may appear we have been villifying the efforts of the organic food movement, we have only tried to give a factual, practical approach to the choice phrases and recommendations of some of the leading advocates. They are using scare tactics and bold, unproven statements to "sell" the program to the public.

And yet, there is a great deal of public value to much of the "teachings". As we pointed out, if nothing else, the movement will help to emphasize an International need for *Nutritional Awareness*.

Today, the term "organic" has come to mean a new life style, a way of "getting it together" in a technologically-oriented society. The return to "natural foods" is more than just a fad!

If you get your "vibrations" from an organic carrot — if you want to take a "trip" the natural way — if your "bag" is to straddle the nutritional fence, you at least won't have to change your religion to appreciate the idea of taking the best from both possible worlds.

MARKETING ORDERS

It was in 1933 that the Agricultural Adjustment Act was quickly approved through a predominantly rural Congress in the midst of a depression. Five years later came the Agricultural Marketing Agreement Act.

At varying times since, State legislatures have passed their own marketing acts, or merely confirmed their own form of "consent" to the Federal act.

Within these State or Federal acts are the "enabling" laws under which the programs operate and under which farmers and others are protected from the antitrust laws.

Rather than attempt to detail the steps required in the formation of a marketing order for a crop, or area of production, suffice to say that marketing orders are a tool of the grower and must have his consent for promulgation. While "ground rules" vary, we will cite the California-Arizona citrus marketing orders which, by law, require that 75% of the producers voting, or producers of two-thirds of the volume produced, must approve the order before it can become operative. Administration of the Order is financed by an assessment of so much per carton of fruit and is deducted by the handler from monies owed to the producer, the former remitting to the Order.

We have never seen a study to indicate how much of the nation's fresh fruits and vegetables are controlled through Marketing Orders, but this would, regardless, vary from year to year. California, leading producer

of the 50 States, has 38 marketing orders and programs under the Act, three of which started in 1937-38, and four of which will be self-eliminating by 1975. Most are for indefinite terms, which can be voted out if enough producers vote against them.

Essentially, Marketing Orders enable producers to correlate the marketing of their products with market demand; establish orderly marketing of commodities; provide methods and means for the maintenance of present markets, or for the development of new or larger markets; or, for prevention, modification or elimination of trade barriers which obstruct the free flow of marketing commodities.

Details of the many facets of a "marketing order" are quite involved and require lengthy explanation. To the student of marketing, he will find the library or Economic Research Service of the U.S.D.A. a ready source.

REGULATORY AGENCIES

The Perishable Agricultural Commodity Act became a law in June, 1930, its purpose being to control interstate commerce on fresh fruits and vegetables. Marketing terms are defined under the Act so that a specific and binding agreement for sale of large or small quantities of fresh produce can be made with a few words. Any controversies that arise within the industry are submitted to PACA authorities for either informal or formal adjudication. Decisions are based on trade terms and definitions promulgated under the Act, as well as precedent cases previously judged within the industry. The Act has helped raise the business standards in the industry to a high level.

In Canada, the counterpart of PACA is "The Fruit, Vegetables and Honey Act."

The purity of foods moving in interstate commerce in the U. S., or imported from foreign countries, is governed by the Federal Food, Drug and Cosmetic Act and the regulations thereunder. This law is enforced by the Food and Drug Administration of the Department of Health, Education and Welfare.

The law and regulations are designed to assure consumers of the receipt of clean, sound, wholesome foods under labeling which is not misleading in any particular. Controls are required by the law and regulations to insure that pesticide residues in, or on, fruit and vegetable products do not present a hazard.

At present, there is no practical method for raising enough food for our big population without using a wide array of chemicals to reduce losses from pests. The industry's use of the chemicals is carried on under regulations imposed by the U. S. Department of Agriculture and the Food and Drug Administration. Space here is insufficient to relate the safeguards employed by growers and packers to assure that fresh product does not contain harmful spray residues.

The Federal Trade Commission was established by Congress in 1914 to protect business and the public against unfair methods of competition and to prevent practices which would lessen competition or tend to create monopoly. The Commission is, in short, charged with the basic duty of protecting our competitive free-enterprise economy.

The above are the basic regulatory agencies controlling conduct of the fresh fruit and vegetable industry in intra- and interstate commerce.

HYDROPONICS—SOILLESS CULTIVATION

Hydroponics is the growing of plants in nutrient solutions without soil, originated during experiments in California a century ago; but it is only during the past thirty years that this novel method of soilless cultivation acquired commercial importance. First, for ornamental plants and flowers, later for vegetables. Hydroponics can be used for cultivation in the open air as well as in greenhouses.

Hydroponic growing was widely used to supply the U. S. Army in Korea with fresh produce and is extensively used by Russian kolkhozes, largely for growing tomatoes and cucumbers. Numerous market gardeners in Germany and Switzerland use it for certain crops and large volumes of melons are grown for export in Europe.

No soil is needed. The only requirement is a nutrient solution of water and minerals containing all the required nutrients for the plant.

Moss, excelsior, straw, or other inert medium, is placed on top of a bed of medium sized gravel in an open tank or waterproof container. The straw or other inert material provides a "bed" in which the seed germinates. The roots of the plant extend down through the gravel and the plant gains its main support in this manner.

When the plants have used up the nutrient in the water, it is drained (or pumped) from the tank and fresh water-laden nutrient is pumped or poured into the large container.

Precise balance of nutrients is possible under this method. Fewer soil pests or parasites, generally less labor; but, initial costs are quite high. The greatest advantage is the rapidity of growth of the products and yields per plant much higher.

"CONTROLLED ATMOSPHERE"

In recent years, the fresh fruit industry has employed a long-range storage method known as controlled atmosphere (C.A.). Its use is increasing.

All fresh fruits continue to respire after harvest; that is, may take on oxygen and give off carbon dioxide. Many fruits ripen after harvest. This ripening process may be greatly retarded by the usual cold storage methods, which reduce fruit metabolism, including the rate of respiration. Under C.A. methods of storage, respiration and ripening may be reduced further by lowering the oxygen content of the air, which normally consists of 21% oxygen, 78% nitrogen and 1% other elements.

Two principal techniques are employed to reduce the percentage of oxygen in C.A. storage rooms. The first involves the use of oxygen and its displacement by carbon dioxide in natural respiration of the fruit. In this process, however, provision must be made to prevent excess accumulation of carbon dioxide, which could be harmful.

The second method involves the circulation of atmosphere of the desired composition (produced by commercial generators) through the storage rooms to replace normal air. By this method, the oxygen content may be lowered sufficiently in a matter of hours, or at most a few days, much faster than by the first method.

Many fruits have been tested in C.A. storage to determine the most suitable atmospheric conditions and temperatures for prolonging their life. These fruits include apples, pears, peaches, grapes, strawberries, bananas, and oranges.

As this is written, the most successful C.A. fruit storage has been for apples and each apple variety differs slightly in requirements for oxygen, carbon dioxide, temperature and relative humidity for optimum results.

For some varieties, C.A. storage has been successful in allowing storage for seven to eight months at 38°F.

Essentials for C.A. storage include airtight rooms and special equipment to achieve and maintain satisfactorily the desired atmospheric conditions. This is in addition to the requirements for adequate refrigeration and air circulation for regular cold storage.

Good quality and condition apples, properly stored in C.A. rooms, hold their condition well from the fall until the following summer. This allows growers and others selling the apples an extended period for marketing the fruit. It permits flexibility in choice of time to market. Consumers also benefit from C.A. storage by providing them with increased quantities of fruit late in the season.

As this is written, an adjunct to the stationary controlled atmosphere storage has come into the picture for the future. This method involves the shipping of fresh fruits and vegetables under "controlled atmosphere" conditions by either truck or rail shipments. This may be product out of a regular C.A. storage area — or direct from a field.

The truck trailer, or rail car, must be airtight. A pressure compensation unit inside the conveyance is necessary to maintain a stable atmosphere, since inside-outside pressure changes. This is supplied by a plastic breather bag installation. The loaded unit is sealed with a plastic curtain consisting of a sprayed-on vinyl material. "Port-hole" receiving valves in the curtain permit exhaust of the original atmosphere and injection (by portable generator) of the new, controlled atmosphere. Regular refrigeration contained in the conveyance maintains desired temperature in the vehicle.

As this is written, very successful shipments have been made with lettuce, apples and strawberries. On addition, the system is being proposed for the home refrigerator.

PACKAGING "FRESH"

As this is written, in the U. S. and Canada, about 40% of all fresh fruits and vegetables are sold retail in consumer size packages or units. The present industry-wide trend indicates that produce sales in consumer unit packages will continue to increase.

Today, in some areas of the U. S., retailers display produce exclusively packaged or unitized. ("Packaged" means product is contained within a tray, box or film-wrapping; "unitized" means several parts placed in a non-wrapped or covered unit, such as a rubber band around several stalks of celery or spears of asparagus; a flexible plastic tape performing the same service.)

Many products are now packaged almost entirely at point of origin; for example, radishes, carrots and cauliflower. A number of centrally-located packaging operations in terminal markets such as Cleveland, Detroit, Boston, New York, etc. package for retailers the semi-perishable and highly perishable products for those retailers desiring packaged or unitized produce departments. Or, a large retail group may maintain its own packaging operation in the distribution center.

Most packaged produce sold today in retail stores is packaged at the store level. While there is some merit to this program, the disadvantages far exceed the advantages. Clerk-hour cost is currently at a premium and will be higher; back-room space for equipment, material and working area is likewise very costly per sq. ft. If a retailer has 40 stores and 40 head produce

clerks, he will also have 40 interpretations of "quality" at the display area — and the necessity to buy 40 complete sets of basic packaging equipment.

A very recent consumer survey revealed a continuing consumer preference for purchasing many fresh fruits and vegetables in bulk form, yet the same consumers admitted buying an abundance of items packaged. Regionally, only consumers in the Northeastern part of the country revealed a slight preference for packaged or unitized fresh product.

Principal objections to packaging: too much (or too little) offered in packages — no variety of unit sizes. Despite the great visibility of today's packages, "they hide the badly bruised or rotten produce in the package". (No progressive retailer would intentionally do this, so the latter objection stems from lack of basic and constant quality control in the already-packaged product — and this can happen in bulk merchandising).

But what about the advantages? Packaging speeds shopping, helps the customer check-out faster. The produce gets less handling, so it should be fresher, cleaner, more sanitary and in better condition, because it does reduce breakage and bruising. The buyer can immediately determine the price of a consumer unit package. Customers' hands are protected from soiling or becoming wet in making the selection, and, it prevents the carry-home paper bag from becoming damp and breaking.

Packaging, through greater utilization of display area, permits greater variety of product offering. Generally, the retailer places the best quality in a package and the last shoppers of the day don't find packaged produce "picked over". Many packages contain useful facts that help the consumer prepare or preserve the product — not possible in bulk. Too, packaged produce requires less space in the home refrigerator, cannot mingle with non-compatible products.

Perhaps the most important advantage is the proven fact that nutritive value of many products is more effectively retained when properly packaged. Dehydration is reduced, inedible portions eliminated.

To those of you who love to see tables and refrigerated racks in the retail store over-flowing with the brilliant colors of fresh, unpackaged produce, we recommend some frequent and long looks of pleasure, for "your" days are numbered!

The very simple economics of cost per square foot of back room and display area, coupled with man-hour costs for the multitude of tasks to perform before the product gets to the display area, will not be economically feasible in the near-future in retail grocers.

Self-service meat is a good example of what will happen to produce. National surveys each year, after self-service meats were inaugurated, showed the homemaker *preferred* service meat departments! But, retail top management had already determined from their own studies they could no longer afford to give the consumer what *she* wanted, since increasing cost for "service" meat departments would prohibit giving the consumer meat at values pre-determined by the consumer.

Packaging, or unitizing, fresh fruits and vegetables has allowed mass retailing to operate more efficiently, and considerably reduced spoilage of the products packaged. These savings more than offset a retailer's need to justify the cost of packaging without increased retails. They can free their operations from the produce scale in the department, which increases efficiency close to 30%!

Of prime consideration in the move to packaging produce is the retailer recognition that there is no "average consumer". Each person entering the produce department has individual wants and desires. Through packaging, retailers are able to serve the individual needs of consumers through the widest choice of sizes and product available, through a rather complex merchandising operation, totally impossible without packaging — whether or not a consumer recognizes this fact.

STORING FRUITS, VEGETABLES

The relative humidity and temperature advice listed throughout this booklet for storage of each commodity is what the industry considers optimum. Here's how to apply to your own equipment:

The crisper tray in your home refrigerator is approximately 38-42°, varying slightly with different makes. The upper level of your refrigerator will be about 3° warmer than the crisper.

In the frost-free type refrigerator, there will be practically no difference in temperature from top to bottom levels.

The approximate relative humidity inside your refrigerator is 40-50%, with exception of the crisper tray. The glass or plastic tray which covers the crisper trays stops, or practically stops, the flow of cold air from circulating inside the crisper trays, thereby raising the humidity in the tray. The colder you set your home refrigerator, the more cold air circulates, resulting in lower humidity.

For general purposes, whether you are a homemaker, shipper or retailer, the object of refrigeration is to prolong storage and shelf-life and to maintain quality by lowering the commodity temperature so that deterioration is retarded. To refrigerate, heat must be removed. Heat is a positive and measurable form of energy. Cold,

on the other hand, is the lack or absence of heat. Cold cannot be given off or radiated.

Heat, however, does radiate. It always flows from the warmer to the cooler object. It is important to remember fresh fruits and vegetables are living things, even though they have been separated from the mother plant, and will continue to generate and give off heat (heat of respiration) as long as they are alive. The amount of heat generated varies with the commodity and its temperature.

Because of the above factors, as well as the wide array of different containers used in the industry — and likewise the difference in size and efficiency of shipping conveyances — the temperatures and humidity recommended for "storage" of the various commodities listed in this book may *not* apply to optimum temperatures and humidities necessary for proper *shipment* of the product, whether domestic or international in scope.

QUALITY, GRADE AND CONDITION

Obviously, not all fresh fruits and vegetables grow to the same degree of perfection, nor are they all of the same uniformity internally. Fresh fruit and vegetable appearance, and life-expectancy, since they are living and breathing things, can be likened to humans.

While no conclusive studies are currently available to suggest humans will look younger and live longer in one section of the country than another, in fresh fruits and vegetables, the climate, soil, weather and district in which a product is grown affects its quality almost as much as the kind of care it received during harvesting, packing and shipping.

With thousands of growers engaged in producing commercial crops for shipment to distant markets, some kind of standard for the industry must exist in order that buying and selling may be carried on effectively. The U. S. Department of Agriculture has established a grading system for fresh produce based on appearance, condition and other factors that might affect eating quality and waste. These grades are established with the cooperation of growers, marketers and technicians throughout the industry who are specialists in each commodity considered. These grade rules, supplemented by State grading regulations, become the basis upon which trading is conducted in the industry.

A distinction should be noted with respect to "grade", "condition" and "quality".

"Quality" denotes the characteristics of a product that are permanent — such as maturity, freedom from insect damage, color, surface blemishes. "Condition" concerns factors in the product that may change, such as decay and internal, unseen factors inherent to that particular piece of product. "Grade", when correlated to U. S. standards established, refers to the sum of the characteristics of the commodity at the time it is graded, including both quality and condition factors.

In purchasing fresh fruits and vegetables, one lot may just meet minimum requirements for a certain grade, while another lot will be considerably above the minimum requirement — yet both lots will be classified as of the same grade.

Some of the Federal classifications for quality are U.S. Extra Fancy, U.S. Fancy, U.S. Extra No. 1, U.S. No. 1, U.S. No. 2. There are other grades of commodities to fit special cases, such as U.S. Combination (a combination of two other grades mentioned above); U.S. No. 1 Bronze (for grapefruit, for instance); U.S. No. 1 Boilers (for onions).

Similarly, produce may be graded to meet the State minimum grade requirements established for a product. The grade is then known as, for example, Virginia Extra Fancy, or, Ohio Commercial, etc. Generally, State minimum grade requirements are lower than Federal minimums. Occasionally, they may be identical.

Some states, in cooperation with the U.S.D.A., establish minimum U.S. grades for some of their products, requiring, for example, that no potatoes shall be shipped failing to meet the minimum requirements of U.S. No. 1. This is generally part of a Marketing Order established by the State and administered by the U.S. Secretary of Agriculture, selected industry members in that State being an advisory board to the Secretary. Thus, compulsory inspection is a requirement of shipment in intra- or interstate commerce, to prove the product meets minimum requirements of the Order.

About 45% of all shipments of fresh fruits and vegetables are officially inspected, mostly at shipping point.

The fee for inspection is paid by the party ordering the inspection. It is a fee based on the quantity and kind of commodity; a published rate for each is established. For a carload, or a large truckload, the fee will average about $18.00. U. S. inspection service may be purchased on a contract, hourly basis, to provide the applicant with continuous quality control on his gradings, if he so desires.

The Federal, State minimum standards are necessarily quite broad and, to a certain extent, flexible. Therefore, some shippers have established outstanding reputations for themselves by shipping under their best labels only produce which conforms to their own high standards. For example, the Blue Goose Trade Mark of Blue Goose, Inc. is universally recognized as standing for "the best of the better crops". You will find the trade mark on more than just a few commodities — it identifies a complete "family" of fresh produce.

TRANSPORTATION — CONSUMPTION — PRODUCTION

Despite some failings, the U.S. food marketing system serves Americans by getting farm products to consumers in the form and at the time they want them. A primary and major part of the system is getting the food products off the farm.

Each year, about 392 million tons of products are transported off U. S. farms — about one ton per cultivated acre. To haul these products, there are over 200,000 miles of railroads, 1.9 million rail cars, 16.8 million trucks and 3.3 million miles of inter-city highways and 26,000 miles of improved waterways. (All 1968 figures.)

Even though most foods are hauled hundreds of miles between producer and consumer, transportation takes only six cents out of the food dollar!

Rail shipment of most highly perishable farm products declined sharply by 1969, and will probably continue. Three important factors contribute to the railroad's loss of perishable tonnage to motor trucks:

1. The railroad advantage in rate-making is directly related to the distance products move. Adjustments in long-haul rates to meet competition cannot be matched by adjustments in short-haul rates.
2. Movement of most agricultural products is exempt from economic regulation by the Interstate Commerce Commission when shipped by motor truck. This permits a large amount of freedom for truckers in contracting for agricultural shipments. (Also, agricultural products are often available for a backhaul by a trucker, rather than return empty.)
3. The service advantage of trucks, which can pick up and deliver products at a number of points for the same load. Firms without rail facilities at their businesses can ship and receive products directly by truck, eliminating double handling. In many cases, truck transportation is faster than movement by rail.

During 1969, eight salad vegetables accounted for over 75 lbs. of the average 98 pounds of fresh vegetables eaten nationally. Lettuce, including escarole, per capita consumption grew from 20 lbs. to 22.2 lbs. from 1960 to 1968. Our appetite for carrots held at around 7 lbs. over those years. Salads also helped buoy up declining fresh use of celery, tomatoes and cabbage.

The average per capita consumption of vegetables in 1960 was, on a fresh weight basis, 106 lbs. of fresh, 82 lbs. of canned and 15 lbs. of frozen, for a national U. S. average of 203 lbs.

In 1969, the same figures had changed to 98 lbs. of fresh, 94 lbs. of canned and 20 lbs. of frozen, for an average of 212.

Experts of the Economic Research Service say per capita vegetable consumption probably won't change from the current figures, at least by 1980.

The percentage of our incomes spent for food slipped another notch in 1969 — down to 16½% per capita after-tax earnings! No other nation in the world can boast of such a low cost!

U. S. consumers in 1969 spent $103.6 billion for all food — an average of $510 per person. Ninety per cent was spent for domestic foods.

One study shows that families with annual incomes of $15,000 and higher spend 12% of their income for food; those with incomes below $1,000 spend more than 50%.

Within U. S. borders, there are 2,266,000,000 acres of land. Agricultural uses — cropland and grazing land — occupy one-half of the area, forests about one-third and the remainder for all other uses. About three acres in five of U. S. land are privately-owned. This includes about 1.3 billion acres of land held by private persons, institutions and companies — and 50 million acres of Indian trust and tribal lands.

On the public's side of the fence, there are some 888 million acres of land. All but 122 million acres of this are owned by the Federal Government. By geographic area, less than 10% of the Government's land is located in the Eastern two-thirds of the country. Most Federal property is divided equally between Alaska and the States in the West.

Over-all, California leads the entire nation in commercial production of 46 crops and livestock commodities. It accounts for about 25% of all U. S. table food, exports $500 million worth of agricultural products and does all this on less than 10% of its land — and less than 3% of the nation's farms.

One of the things that makes California agriculture famous is that just about everything grown anywhere in the U. S. is raised there and many items produced in California are grown practically no place else in the nation!

California produces 100% of the U. S. ladino clover seed, 99.6% of its artichokes, 99% of the alfalfa seed, 99% of its dates, nectarines, olives, plums, chili peppers, pomegranates and prunes; 97% of its apricots, 90% of the walnuts, 92% of the garlic and grapes, 89% of the brussels sprouts, 85% of the broccoli; 65% of the cantaloupes,

cauliflower, lettuce and tomatoes, 60% of the peaches, 59% of the celery, 48% of the lima beans, 43% of the carrots, etc.

MARKETING "FRESH"

The marketing of fresh fruits and vegetables is dominated by one central theme: a tremendous sense of urgency, because of the perishable nature of the products.

Huge volumes must be harvested, graded, packed, pre-cooled, sold, loaded on proper transportation and delivered. If, from the grower on up, everyone has done his job correctly, the product arrives "fresh".

Large volumes must be moved to market in relatively brief periods. Supplies are highly variable, not only within a season, but also from year to year — whether row crop or tree crop. Both the vagaries of weather, and many times the uncoordinated production of growers, may operate to bring about sudden shortages or surpluses.

Through these highly fluid conditions, product must move swiftly to consumers, with the industry apparently better able to meet the physical challenges of distribution, than to deal with the economic problems.

Growers may also be packers and sellers. Growers may join a cooperative, the latter harvesting, grading, selling. Generally, a grower signs a marketing contract with a cooperative or corporate to perform all functions except growing.

Prior to World War II, most fresh fruits and vegetables were consigned or sold to jobber-wholesalers in terminal markets located generally in highly-populated urban areas. Or, were sold on auctions located in St. Louis, Chicago, Detroit, Cleveland, Baltimore, Philadelphia, Boston and New York. Sales through either method were made to retailers, purveyors, secondary jobbers and large jobber-wholesalers.

Much of this has changed today. Now, less than half of the U. S. production is sold by terminal market operators and/or auctions. Instead, integrated voluntary or cooperative groups, and much larger corporate retailers, are by-passing the terminal with buyers at shipping points, or, "direct" buying. Also, better roads, better truck equipment have permitted the usual broker to engage in a "jobbing" business of his own in the interest of his principals.

For example, a broker will solicit business for Washington apples from six different receivers in perhaps as many cities or towns. He passes the order on to his shipper, the shipper secures a truck, the truck makes "drop" shipments to these six receivers in the quantity desired by each.

In many instances, several commodities may be placed on the truck in proper unloading sequence, each of the six receivers being delivered the quantity and quality of each product ordered. This is called a "pool" shipment.

The receiver may be a corporate, voluntary or cooperative chain — or a jobber, wholesaler or secondary jobber.

The direct buying by large groups is having a strong and continuing effect on the industry.

The auctions are becoming specialty distributors rather than mass distributors. Sales of higher-valued fruits are holding up much better than those of lower-priced, large-quantity items. Larger wholesalers and chains (corporate, voluntary and cooperative) prefer to buy their large volume items directly from shipping point.

Reasons for change in the fruit and vegetable industry include broad social and economic forces, such as population growth, rising levels of living, increased urbanization and changes in consumers' tastes. Too, there have been new and improved varieties of crops, improved technology in production and processing, more rapid and efficient communication facilities and faster and more dependable transportation.

Historically, prices secured by terminal markets (jobbers or auctions) were the guide to pricing of product at shipping point — basically, the law of supply and demand. The multitude of firms "competing" for shipping point product — the great number of firms "competing" for product at the auction or terminal — created a market for the merchandise.

Today, to a great extent, the place where price is determined has been relocated to scattered areas of production. Shipping point selling tends to make price discovery more obscure. Large buyers reveal neither the volumes they purchase, the price they pay, nor their future buying plans.

Mass merchandising has induced greater inflexibility into the pricing system. Consumer shopping habits have reduced the pressure on supermarkets to establish retail prices which closely follow wholesale price changes. Instead, retail price adjustments are delayed until product costs justify changes in relation to retail profit objectives and psychological pricing structure. This insensitivity of retail pricing makes it difficult to "clean up" a glut of supplies, except for a very major change in prices at shipping point.

This seeming "insensitivity" is the result of mass retailers pre-planning and pre-ordering from suppliers to meet specific merchandising plans. Thus, with most of the commodities available direct from shipping point through direct buying, or the retailer's own purchasing agent or broker, supplies are pre-planned for well in advance of actual, prospective sale at the retail level.

Despite the declining role of the terminal market in product distribution, they remain a major factor in distributing all fresh fruits and vegetables to a large element of independent retailers, purveyors — and are the source for even major retail chains when the latter's store orders are larger than he anticipated seven to ten days previously in ordering his shipment from his buyer or shipper at the source. Likewise, on the highly perishable commodities, particularly the exotics, and historically slow-moving-at-retail items, the terminal operator remains a valuable factor.

With fewer buyers for product, growers and shippers have — all too slowly — integrated, combined, acquired one another, to have a more meaningful tonnage for the large buyer, to gain their rightful position in the bargaining system. Part of the bargaining power of the larger sellers is in their control of Marketing Orders.

While old-timers in the fresh fruit and vegetable industry find great fault with the present system and trend in product distribution, it is a proven fact that one element in the industry has been harmed more than any other in his share of the fresh food dollar: the grower.

It is a simple law of marketing economics that when there are too many sellers appealing to too few buyers, the one who owns (or made) the product has to be harmed.

In "merchandising" — whether it be grower, shipper, broker, jobber or retailer — true movement of product occurs only at the point-of-sale. Until it gets into the hands of the consumer, and satisfaction is given, nobody can claim the product is really sold. Previous to that, everyone has only transferred title.

The buyer and merchandiser for the retailer has an obligation to present the consumer with the right product, moving in the right quantity, to the right place, at the right price, at the right time.

It is rather strange that the same descriptive product obligation applies to the grower and shipper, and yet there is a constant battle of marketing wits among all factors in marketing the fresh product.

There are several implications for the near and long-range future, principally that there will be a greater need for shippers and packers to be managers, rather than traders.

FOOD RETAILING

Food retailing is in for a period of unprecedented change within the next few years! Demographic studies indicate retail chain store supermarkets, as we know them today, with 6-10,000 items, will become vastly larger stores (with greatly increased consumer services), costing a million dollars or more to build, and carrying 15,000 items — but there will be fewer stores!

On the other hand, the "convenience" store, a commercial "mom and pop", with limited variety, will also become more commonplace.

There is new management attention to the fact that the *"average"* customer doesn't exist! And there are sharp differences in the *kinds* of customers who patronize one store as compared to another.

But this is only the beginning! Demographic studies involve family income, age, whether mostly female or male shoppers, family size and composition, distance from the store and frequency of shopping trips.

Type of shopper, *i.e.*, white collar, blue collar, retired, farmer — whether you're white or colored, part of an ethnic group — and type of neighborhood — are all considerations for store placement and type of merchandising approach management will take.

Since the "super" supermarket of the future will be centrally located to serve larger areas of population, and yet readily accessible to the more mobile American, all the above factors in demographic studies, plus merchandise selection, store layout, greater variety of product and better advertising and promotion, will become vital.

And there is growing consideration for the two, primary needs of consumers: the biological *necessities*, the psychological *wants*. Bread, hamburger, potatoes and sugar fall in the category of biological necessities; shrimp, steak, kiwi fruits are psychological wants.

As recently as the 1950's, 75% of our people went to a restaurant because they were hungry; now, most people go to a restaurant for pleasure, to enjoy dining. Homes are not merely shelters, they are designed and decorated. A number of years ago, a man bought a car because he needed transportation — he now buys attractively-styled cars that give him transportation, but the transportation is taken for granted.

Selling a pleasure — the psychological wants — is not the same as selling the biological needs of, for example, mere shelter or transportation.

Thus, there is greater attention to merchandising products in food stores that are designed for pleasure, not for maintaining life. This is a product of our society of abundance and psychological values. But, they must be sold by employing *psychological devices*.

To achieve maximum sales, a food store operator must expose every customer to as many items — as many influences — as possible, per shopping trip. Prime consideration must be given to net profit per square foot of store area: thus, the reason for more shelving in the grocery section, more multi-level refrigerated cases in produce — to accommodate more commodities; the reason for the attractive color schemes, the "motivational packaging", the height of the display of some products, the merchandising emphasis in ads and at the store level with respect to season of the year — whether it was a pay day in that store area. Open dating, dual pricing, nutrition labeling — all have an influence on how the consumer is appealed to in the merchandising effort.

The number of grocery stores in the U. S. declined from 260,000 in 1960 to 208,300 at the close of 1970. Most of this decline has occurred among small and/or unaffiliated stores. (A small store is one doing less than $100,000 a year in total sales.)

The number of supermarkets, those considered doing $500,000 or more in annual sales, has increased to 38,300, compared to 33,000 in 1960.

The medium size store, called by many a "superette", has declined in number to 33,500 — these are stores having annual sales of $150-500,000.

The share of business enjoyed by the supermarkets has increased from 69% in 1960 to 75.4% of the total at the close of 1970; this on only 18.4% of the total number of stores in the U. S.!

Despite the seeming dominance of the corporate chain, the independent, affiliated store has done well in recent years. In 1970, as a group, they achieved a sales gain of 12.3%, slightly higher than the 10.3% for chains.

Stimulated by a recession, "discount supers" surged forward in their sales, and the trend will probably continue. In 1970, 34% of all supermarkets merchandised the "discount" technique with a resultant loss of only 2½% of their margin — but an average sales gain of almost 25% over their former methods!

The continued growth of the convenience store has been phenomenal — from a national total of 500 in 1957 to 13,250 stores in 1970. In the same period, they rose from .2% of the U. S. food store sales to 3%, stocked an average of 3,205 items, had an average size of 2,389 sq. ft.

It is obvious from the trend, the independent retailer is being forced to give up most of his independence to survive and grow, for the dominant trend in food retailing is giantism. To compete, even with a convenience store, the independent must now join his fellows to form giant independent chains under a voluntary or cooperative banner. In this way he will continue a competitive factor with the advantages of central buying, warehousing and delivery — and sharing the cost of expensive "staff" services for planning and merchandising.

FRUITS

APPLES

Historians tell us that the apple was known to ancient cavemen and to the Early Greeks and Romans — perhaps not in the succulent form in which expert horticulturists give it to you today, but nevertheless with many of the desirable eating qualities which make it known as the "King of Fruits".

And King Apple is still the all-American fruit, according to a national consumer survey conducted recently. Apples are purchased with some regularity by 93% of U. S. families, the survey found, compared to 92% who regularly buy and eat bananas and 83% fresh oranges. As expected, the Red Delicious variety led all the rest in terms of consumer awareness and preference, with 95% of the primary food buyers acquainted with this variety.

Too many housewives buy apples without regard to variety and, consequently, fail to get the best the market affords. There is no such thing as the typical apple flavor, as each variety has its own distinctive taste — sweet, mellow, or tart, as the case may be. Some apples are better suited for baking, some for eating out of hand, while others make better sauce because of their firmness of flesh as well as their flavor characteristics. There are *7,000* varieties of apples grown in the U. S. and listed by the Department of Agriculture's division of plant industry. Of these varieties, *13* provide about 90% of the total production.

Washington State is the largest producer of apples, followed by New York, Michigan, California, Pennsylvania and Virginia — with these six states accounting for approximately 71% of total production. Other important states include West Virginia, North Carolina, Ohio, New Jersey, Oregon, Illinois, Colorado, Maryland, Wisconsin, Idaho and Missouri.

Commercial apple production is dominated by only nine leading varieties. Delicious is the leader, accounting for 27.9% of the total. The nine leaders make up 82.6% of the total commercial production.

The second spot in variety ranking goes to Golden Delicious, followed by McIntosh, Rome, Jonathan, York, Stayman, Winesap and Newtown Pippin.

It is unfortunate that few consumers fail to recognize that the domestically-grown Newtown Pippin — a green apple — is truly an all-purpose apple! Most people automatically classify a green apple as a cooking apple

— *only*. Grown mainly in Oregon, California and Washington, the Newtown has a flesh that is hard, crisp, juicy and with an acidity that is medium to above-medium. For most of the season, the skin color is green, is good for salads, desserts or cooking. Since it is a hardy apple and keeps well, the marketing season extends from late fall into June.

Another fine, green-skinned apple, but in this case relatively new on the scene, is the imported Granny Smith. Somewhat similar in size, shape and uses to the domestically-grown Newtown Pippin, the Granny Smith is principally grown in South Africa, New Zealand and Australia, is imported into North America beginning in March or early April.

Very popular in recent years is the development of new Red Sport varieties for greater eye appeal and flavor, primarily designed for the fresh market. (A "sport" is a sudden, spontaneous deviation or variation of an organism from type, beyond the usual limits of individual variation.) Apple growers are on the lookout for tree limbs that show fruit with favorable variations, such as more red color, or color that comes out on the apple earlier than the rest of the tree. Many new Sports are announced every year and new Sports are already becoming a Super-Sport. Some of the Sports are spur-type trees on which fruit spurs are formed along large scaffold limbs and fruit is produced on practically all parts of the tree.

Apples are usually harvested in bulk wooden containers holding the equivalent of approximately 25 boxes (40# per box) of apples. They are mechanically forklifted from the orchards to trucks that convey them to the packing houses.

After the bulk bins are brought to the packing house, the entire bin is immersed in a huge vat of water. Leading away from this water reservoir are metal channels, also filled with water. The apples, being lighter than the water, float to the top and gently ride on the water down the troughs. A pump at the bottom of the water reservoir keeps the water circulating away from the reservoir, down the troughs and into the sizing and grading mechanism.

Besides eliminating any possibility of spray residue remaining on the apples, the fruit is cushioned by the water in thus being removed from the bulk bin and conveyed to the grading-packing area.

In recent years, and the practice will probably increase, all apple varieties are waxed — a thin layer of tasteless and harmless wax which retards moisture loss and increases store and home "life" of the apples.

The "boxed apple" has practically become a misnomer. Today, in national marketings, more apples are shipped in polyethylene bags (3#, 4# and larger, up to 10# units) than any other single container. In shipping, these "poly" bags are unitized into corrugated containers called "masters".

Another method of consumer packaging is the over-wrapped tray — a small or large pulp or plastic tray holding from 4-12 apples (depending on tray size), over-wrapped with a clear film to immobilize the apples and yet permit ready inspection. Such packages are packed at shipping point, terminal market or store level.

The very tender, but delectable, varieties — such as the Golden Delicious and the McIntosh — are very frequently shipped in a corrugated container called a "cell" pack. With specially-designed vertical and horizontal dividers in each layer, the dividers extend above the height of the apples and provide a "cell" in which each apple is placed. The layers of cells are then divided by flat pieces of corrugated.

With labor costs increasing, the trend in some areas of production is toward bulk shipments. Almost completely mechanized, freshly harvested apples, after grading, are placed in a corrugated container with about 40# of fruit. Another method employed for the same purpose, principally for what is known as terminal market packaging, is the shipping of complete bulk bins (used for harvesting purposes, generally) which contain approximately 800-1,000# of fruit each.

Most of the balance of the production is shipped in what is commonly known in the industry as a "tray pack", with dividers placed between the layers of apples, each divider having a "cup" indenture to hold the apples.

The size of apples is still described in terms of the number of apples contained in a box: 48s, for example, are extremely large apples, while 216s are the smallest which are commercially packed.

The most widely used standard of maturity used by orchardists is the pressure test. Similar to the oldtime hand scale, the plunger of the tester is pressed against the surface of the apple after a thin layer of peeling has been removed. The amount of pressure, as recorded by the instrument, required to cause an indenture of approximately ¼", determines whether the apple is hard, firm, firm-ripe or ripe.

Another method employed to determine maturity is a refractometer. A wedge of flesh is cut from the apple, squeezed to secure a drop of juice, placed on a glass slide enclosed in the telescope-like refractometer. By holding it up to the light, the tester can automatically determine, from a self-enclosed gauge, the amount of sugar in that drop of juice.

In a general way, the grade of an apple is not so much determined upon the general defects of its skin, as it is of its color. The Extra Fancy or U. S. Fancy grade apples being more colorful (for variety) than others. Although there is more taste appeal to a fully-colored red apple, the same variety of apples with some bright, red color — and no greenish or sallow coloring — could also provide the same taste pleasure; and, will probably cost you *considerably less.*

In selecting apples, secure those that have good color for their variety and are firm to the touch. This latter point is particularly important when buying the large sizes. Big apples tend to mature more rapidly than the smaller ones and, when soft, usually have a mealy or mushy texture with an over-ripe flavor too mellow for real taste enjoyment.

Here are a few points to bear in mind when buying apples. Those that measure 2½" or more in diameter are ideal for general all-around use. The larger sizes (3" and up) of the baking varieties are best for that purpose. This does not mean that those smaller should be neglected entirely, for they are often priced so as to be more economical for cooking than the larger ones. Check the skins — they should be smooth, reasonably bruise free; too many bruises end up as decay spots, indicating too ripe or too poorly handled. Don't pinch them — you may add another bruise.

Light russet doesn't hurt the quality or the flavor. Are the apples bright and sparkly? On red varieties, the background color should be a slightly yellowish-green — the darker and greener the green, the more immature the apple — too green a ground color will indicate poor flavor, too starchy and hard.

Warm temperatures hasten the ripening process and cause apples to lose their crispness and tangy flavor very rapidly. If you keep reserve supplies in the refrigerator or some equally cool spot, they will be at their best when you are ready to use them.

The availability of fresh, crisp, juicy apples throughout the winter and into the spring depends largely upon scientific cold storage. After November 1, virtually all apples come from storage. Two principal methods of storage are employed — regular cold storage with temperatures maintained around the 30° mark, and CA (controlled atmosphere) storage (see front area of this manual for explanation).

Apples are not particularly noted for their high content of any one vitamin, but they are rich in other healthful substances . . . pectin and fruit acids, for example, as well as minerals. Raw apples are a great help in combating intestinal disorders, as they have properties which aid the digestice juices in killing germs in the stomach.

GOLDEN DELICIOUS

JONATHAN

McINTOSH

NEWTOWN

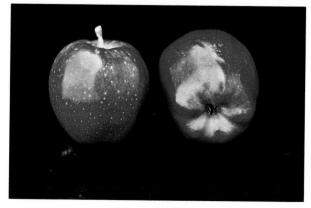

RED DELICIOUS

ROME BEAUTY

WHITE ASTRACHAN

WINESAP

"Blue Goose" is the world's largest marketer of apples. Skookum Packers Association, Wenatchee, Wash., with whom Blue Goose, Inc. is affiliated, is the world's foremost packer-shipper of Golden Delicious apples.

TO YOUR HEALTH: In recent studies, it was revealed that pectin in apples helps to keep cholesterol count down. It was also found that college students, eating two or three apples a day, had less than half as many colds and headaches as their fellow students. Weight control diets many times recommend apples, for a medium-sized apple has only 90 calories; it is "bulk producing", so it satisfies your hunger while the natural sugars give you quick energy. It was also found that an apple is nature's toothbrush — it cleans the teeth, massages the gums, and one apple removes over 30% more bacteria from the mouth than a three-minute brushing plus a gargle! It's true!

COOK YOUR OWN: Apple sauce is the most popular apple product and consists generally of a blend of two or more varieties. When making your own apple sauce, use very little water — add only enough to keep the apples from scorching. Do not add any water to making of pies, Betties, etc. And be careful about sugar — a little highlights the natural apple goodness, depending upon tartness of apples used — too much spoils the natural flavor and makes them mushy.

APPLE TIPS: Are you mystified by the difference in "apple juice" and "apple cider"? These products are the natural, undiluted juice of apples. "Unclarified" is juice "as is". "Clarified" is filtered apple juice to remove all pulp. A preservative is often added. "Cider" is fresh crushed juice in season. "Juice" is pasteurized, canned or bottled for longer season marketing.

Preventing discoloration of peeled apples: Place slices

DESIRABILITY OF VARIOUS APPLE VARIETIES FOR DIFFERENT USES

VARIETY	Flavor and Texture	Fresh & Salad	Pie	Sauce	Baking	Freezing (slices)	Main Season
BEACON	Mild, Mellow	Good	Fair	Excl.	Fair	Fair	Aug.-Sept.
CORTLAND	Mild, Tender	Excl.	Excl.	V. Good	Good	V. Good	Oct.-Jan.
RED DELICIOUS	Sweet, Mellow	Excl.	Poor	Fair	Poor	Fair	Sept.-June
GOLDEN DELICIOUS	Sweet, Semi-firm	Excl.	Excl.	V. Good	V. Good	V. Good	Sept.-May
FENTON	Mild, Mellow	Good	Fair	Excl.	Fair	Fair	Aug.-Sept.
GRANNY SMITH	Tart-Crisp	V. Good	V. Good	V. Good	V. Good	V. Good	April-July
GRAVENSTEIN	Tart-Crisp	Good	Good	Good	Good	Good	July-Sept.
R.I. GREENING	Slightly tart, Firm	Poor	Excl.	Excl.	V. Good	Excl.	Oct.-Mar.
JERSEY RED	Mild, Firm	Good	V. Good	V. Good	Excl.	V. Good	Oct.-Apr.
JONATHAN	Tart, Tender	V. Good	V. Good	V. Good	Poor	V. Good	Sept.-Jan.
LODI	Tart, Soft	Fair	V. Good	V. Good	Poor	Good	July-Aug.
McINTOSH	Slightly tart, Tender	Excl.	Excl.	Good	Fair	Good	Sept.-June
NEWTOWN PIPPIN	Sl. tart, Firm	V. Good	Excl.	Excl.	V. Good	Excl.	Sept.-June
ROME BEAUTY	Slightly tart, Firm	Good	V. Good	V. Good	Excl.	V. Good	Oct.-June
STARR	Tart, Soft	Poor	V. Good	V. Good	V. Good	Good	July-Aug.
STAYMAN	Tart, Semi-firm	V. Good	Good	Good	Good	Good	Oct.-Mar.
WEALTHY	Tart, Soft	Good	Good	V. Good	Fair	Poor	Aug.-Dec.
WINESAP	Slightly tart, Firm	Excl.	Good	Good	Good	V. Good	Oct.-June
YELLOW TRANSPARENT	Tart, Soft	Poor	Excl.	Good	Poor	Poor	July-Aug.
YORK IMPERIAL	Tart, Firm	Fair	Good	V. Good	Good	Good	Oct.-April
WILLIAMS E. RED	Slightly tart, Semi-firm	Fair	Good	Fair	Good	Good	July-Aug.

as they are peeled into a pan of cold water, in which a pinch of salt has been added, for each whole apple peeled.

Peeling quickly: If you're going to cook apples, dip them quickly in and out of boiling water. The skin will come off much more readily.

Leaking pies: Sprinkling salt on spilled juice from apple pies in a hot oven will cause the juice to burn crisply, making it easier to remove.

Aluminum discoloration: Discoloration of aluminum utensils can be removed just as effectively by boiling a number of apple peelings in them as by the old method of boiling a little vinegar in water.

APRICOTS

Fresh apricots, which date back to the days of the ancient Persians, are a delicacy sure to be enjoyed. They have a flavor entirely different from that of the dried variety and are available in the early to mid-summer months from Oregon, Washington, Utah, Idaho and California, with the latter state providing approximately 96% of the total supply.

Golden-yellow color, plumpness and firmness are indications of quality in apricots. Since they are an extremely delicate fruit, you should avoid buying those that are soft to the touch or have a wilted or shriveled look about them. Such fruit decays quickly and lacks good flavor.

Dietitians tell us that apricots rank high in their Vitamin A content. Six medium fresh apricots can supply more than one-third of the normal daily requirement of this important food element. This is one of the best fruit sources of minerals. One apricot has 18 calories.

Apricots are fine for eating fresh, out-of-hand, in fresh fruit salads, fruit cocktails, served with cream, in shortcakes, upside-down cakes, pies, dumplings, souffle or whip. Apricot fritters are an unusual dessert when served with fruit sauce or meat accompaniment.

The three principal varieties of this delicacy are the Moorpark, Royal and Tilton, with other popular varieties being the Blenheim, King Derby and Perfection.

AVOCADOS

The history of the avocado industry in the U. S. is traced back to the Spaniards, with the first recorded importation in 1833 by Henry Perrine. However, proof of the existence of avocados in Mexico, Central and South America as early as 291 B.C. can be found in the Mayan records and Aztec picture writing.

A number of years ago, avocados were considered a thing of luxury, but today, national production and year-around availability from principally California and Florida, have made this delicacy a common table item. The best are identified on the individual fruit, "Blue Goose".

Avocados vary widely in weight, texture, shape and thickness of skin, while the color may range from green to black, depending on the type of fruit and the section of the country in which it was produced. In any case you should avoid those that have dark, soft, sunken spots on their surface or appear badly bruised, for the flesh beneath is sure to be affected.

Avocados are best for eating when they yield to light pressure on the outer rind. Like pears and bananas, they may be purchased slightly under-ripe and ripen at ordinary room temperatures. When fully ripened and ready to eat, the fruit will have a soft, oily-textured flesh and a very rich flavor.

Don't cut an avocado until it is ripe! Besides the above method of testing for ripeness, the very simple way is to stick a toothpick in the fruit at the stem end. If it flows freely in and out of the fruit, it is ripe, ready to eat.

There is a multitude of varieties of avocados — some authorities say better than 700 — with 80% of all avocados grown in the U. S.; following are the principal varieties.

FUERTE. The production leader of the California varieties. It is almost ideally adapted to market requirements as to size, color, long season of maturity. The fruit is green, pear-shaped, 8-16 oz., thin, pliable and a leathery somewhat-pebbled skin. The flavor is very good.

HASS. The second leading variety from California and the chief summer variety. The bulk of California's new plantings are in this variety, which is marketed from April through the following October. It is ovoid shaped, with a thick skin which protects it from the hot summer sun. The color ranges from emerald green at maturity, through black, as it becomes ready to eat.

BACON and *ZUTANO.* The two principal varieties, which, with Fuerte, make up the "fall and winter" crop. Both are pear-shaped, green, thin-skinned.

RINCON and *MAC ARTHUR.* Combined with Hass, make up the "spring and summer" supply of "greens". Pear-shaped, with a medium-thick green skin.

NABAL. Almost round, smooth and green.

ANAHEIM. Pear-shaped, green fruit.

REED. A round, green fruit.

All the above are California varieties of importance. Florida varieties, in order of commercial importance,

ROYAL APRICOT

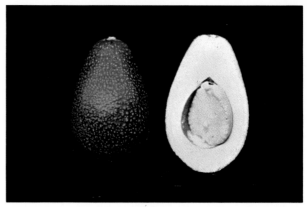

BACON

FUERTE

HASS, GREEN-RIPE

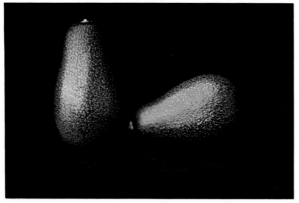

JALNA

ZUTANO

COCKTAIL

22

are vastly different and listed as follows:

BOOTH 8 and *BOOTH 7.* Booth 8 is oblong-ovate, small to medium large, medium green, rather dull skin that is slightly roughened. Booth 7 fruit is rounded obovate, medium size, bright green with slightly pebbled, glossy skin.

LULA. Fruit is pyriform, or occasionally necked, medium large, light green with a nearly smooth skin.

WALDIN. Oblong to oval with a characteristic flattening on one side of the blossom end, medium to large, pale green to greenish yellow in color, and a smooth skin.

The bland flavor and smooth texture of the avocado blend well with almost all other foods. It has a distinctive, appetizing flavor and is generally used in this country as an appetizer or salad. However, devotees of the avocado claim its use as a food is limited only by the user's imagination. For breakfast with scrambled eggs, or mashed and spread on toast. For lunch, avocado sandwich or avocado cubes added to soup. Some like just the thinly sliced avocado with a sprinkling of salt and pepper and lemon or lime juice. It may be served in the half-shell and with a variety of dressings. The seed cavity makes a natural container for other fruits, vegetables, cheese, meat or seafood. May be peeled and sliced, or diced for salad combinations. This fruit goes well in almost every salad. The avocado is the basic ingredient of a popular Mexican and American dish, *guacamole.*

Avocados have eleven vitamins and seventeen minerals. They are a good source of Vitamins A and C, Niacin, Folic Acid, and Vitamin E, as well as an excellent source of potassium, iron and magnesium. Low in sodium, 100 grams (3½ ozs.) of avocado provide approximately 167 calories — and contain no cholesterol!

BANANAS

The banana was probably one of the first plants to be cultivated, and its evolution and migration accompanied that of man from their place of common origin somewhere in southern Asia. The earliest historical reference to the fruit was 327 B.C., when Alexander the Great found it flourishing in India. Traders in the Indian Ocean carried the banana to the eastern coast of Africa, and Chinese traders introduced the banana to the Polynesians before the second century A.D.

Although generations of Yankee seamen and whalers had long been aware of the health benefits of this tropical fruit, the people of North America had to wait over 300 years to have fresh bananas every day on their food menu.

Today bananas are one of the most sought after items in the produce department. Their daily availability, their high nutritional and health value, as well as their universal appeal to all age groups, are the main reasons for this popularity. Because for so long they have been so plentiful and so inexpensive compared to other foods, people of the U.S. and Canada generally do not realize how fortunate they have been to have this tropical fruit available day after day in all seasons.

There are two principal varieties of bananas imported from the tropics: the Gros Michel is the variety that was prominent in retail stores many years ago, almost a rarity now. Generally a long type with a tapered point, it has a pleasant flavor, ripens uniformly and generally is highly resistant to bruising and discoloration. In the tropics, the plant is very susceptible to Panama disease, and thus, the present and future production will probably be reduced.

The leading variety today is the Cavendish. The variety has been under cultivation for many years but it requires a greater degree of care to prevent bruising in handling and shipping, as well as advanced techniques in obtaining uniform ripening results. In the tropics, the plant is immune to the Panama disease. The distinguishing feature of the variety is that the fruit tips are blunt and generally curved.

A small quantity of small-fingered red bananas is also imported into the U.S. and Canada.

The apple banana is a form of the Lacatan variety—small, blunt-fingered fruit similar to the Cavendish but not more than 3-5 inches long. Like red bananas, they are limited in production, bruise quite easily and are heavier in sugar content.

For years, the leading exporter of bananas has been Ecuador, with Honduras a poor second, followed by Costa Rica and Panama. Ecuador, alone, exports 2,631,000,000 lbs. of bananas annually! The leading banana importer is the U.S., annually approximately 3,600,000,000 lbs., with Japan the second largest importer with 1,628,000,000 lbs.

Few American food shoppers remember the large bunch of bananas hanging in the window of the corner grocery store. In those days, the final selection was made by the fruit man or the customer. Now selection and grading is done in the tropics 1500 to 2000 miles away. Waste and unnecessary handling have been eliminated, and a better quality banana is the result. It is one of two fruits that tastes better when it is not tree ripened. Consequently, it is shipped in the green state and ripened domestically in specially equipped rooms.

A great deal of time and effort is being expended to

REGULAR BANANA

PLANTAIN

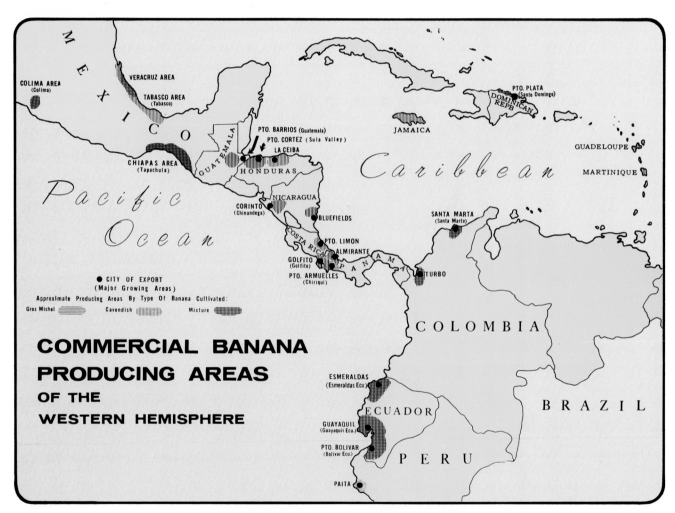

COMMERCIAL BANANA PRODUCING AREAS OF THE WESTERN HEMISPHERE

● CITY OF EXPORT
(Major Growing Areas)

Approximate Producing Areas By Type Of Banana Cultivated:

Gros Michel   Cavendish   Mixture

deliver properly ripened bananas to the retail store and to display them in a way that enables the shopper to select fruit that meets her particular needs. In making her selection, she should select bananas that are not quite full yellow. If she does this, they will be firm and free of bruises when she gets them home. At home they will continue the ripening process if kept at room temperature. Once they have reached the stage of ripeness best suited to the individual taste, they can be placed in the refrigerator and held for several days if desired. (The skin will turn dark in several hours, when refrigerated, but the edible portion will remain unchanged for 3-6 days, then begin to discolor.)

Bananas can be cooked at any stage of ripeness, but generally retain their shape when the skin is still slightly green. They are excellent baked or boiled.

Mashed bananas can be utilized as an ingredient in cakes, bread, cookies and milk shakes — use them for these purposes when the fruit is fully ripe.

Bananas contain only a trace of fat, and this portion

is highly unsaturated. They are satisfying and filling, lessening the desire to over-eat. Easily digested, pediatricians generally recommend ripe bananas as the first solid food for infants.

Bananas have an alkaline effect in the body, help maintain good body chemistry; they are frequently recommended in the dietary management of simple diarrhea and constipation. The sodium content is very low, making them an excellent food for people who are on restricted diets.

When fully ripe, the calorie content for one medium banana is only 88, contains 12 minerals and 6 vitamins — close to an ideal food!

PLANTAIN. See separate section in the "Variety" portion of this book.

BERRIES

A berry is defined as any fleshy, simple fruit with one or more seeds and a skin. True berries include the banana, cranberry, grape and tomato.

BLACKBERRIES-DEWBERRIES. The two great centers of wild blackberries are eastern North America and Europe. Originally, when North America was settled, blackberries were not abundant due to the heavy forests. However, as land was cleared, blackberries spread. Cultivation of the blackberry was not begun apparently until about 1825. In 1875, the dewberry was discovered in West Virginia and transplanted to Ohio. Dewberries are trailing, ground-running kinds of blackberries, while the blackberry is one of the bramble fruits, and grows on an erect plant. As marketed, they look so much alike, they cannot be distinguished.

Boysenberries are a dewberry variety grown mainly in California, but also to some extent in Oregon and Texas. Berries are large and long, 1¼″ long by 1″ thick, dark reddish-black when fully ripe, and slightly acid.

Loganberries are of California origin and is the oldest trailing blackberry variety of the Pacific Coast. Berries are large, long, dark red, acid and high-flavored.

The *Olallie* berry is grown extensively in California, but is of Oregon origin. It is a cross between Black Logan and Young; berries bright black, medium-sized, firm. Principally for local shipments.

BLUEBERRIES. In 1616, an explorer found Indians near Lake Huron gathering blueberries to store for the winter. They dried the berries in the sun, beat them into a powder and added this powder to parched meal. Today, blueberries are the third most popular non-citrus fruit in the U.S. While they are found on almost every continent of the world, the U.S. and Canada grow more blueberries commercially than the rest of the world

combined, both nations are large consumers.

In the U.S., fresh blueberries begin coming to market in May and continue through September, with July the peak month. In May and June, supplies originate in North Carolina, July from New Jersey and late July and August into September from Michigan — the principal fresh market producing states.

Blueberries can be classed as a convenience food because there is no pitting, no peeling, no puttering and no waste! A pint serves four people generously — and they are good for the weight watcher, since a half-cup serving contains only 44 calories. Fresh blueberries are a good source of Vitamin A and C, as well as potassium, phosphorus and calcium.

CRANBERRIES. Long before the Pilgrims landed on our shores, Indians were using glossy red berries (cranberries) for medicine and food. Early settlers picked the fruit from the bogs by hand and later with wooden rake-tooth scoops. Today, mechanical pickers harvest an annual crop of 200,000,000 pounds. Massachusetts and Wisconsin produce the largest supply with New Jersey, Washington and Oregon contributing a substantial share. Unlike the wild berries of long ago, today's fruit is cultivated to grow larger, brighter in color and more flavorful.

Fresh cranberry size, shape and color will depend on the variety. As a general rule they all are glossy, firm, plump and red. Poor quality is indicated by shriveling, dull appearance, softness or stickiness. While cranberries keep longer than most berries, they do need to be stored in the refrigerator. They may be left in their store container and just before cooking time, rinse in cold water and remove any stems or bruised fruit.

During the peak months, September through January, extra berries may be purchased to freeze — a process as simple as placing the unopened bag or box in the freezer. Come cooking time, wash and pick over the berries — no thawing needed. One pound of fruit measures four cups and makes about one quart of whole berry or jellied sauce.

Chemically, the cranberry consists of water, plant fibers, sugar, pectin, waxy materials, protein and the various ash constituents such as calcium, magnesium, potassium and phosphorus, plus various vitamins. There are only 26 calories in 3½ ounces!

With today's convenience foods and instants, the tart flavor of cranberries can be enjoyed a great many ways. A perennial with chicken and turkey dinners, and for that matter, with almost any meat. As a topper for ice cream, plain cake or custard; or as a glaze for baked ham. Garnishing a salad or meat platter or open-faced sandwiches, cranberries have real versatility to make

BLUEBERRIES

RED RASPBERRIES

STRAWBERRIES

BLACKBERRIES

GOOSEBERRIES

CRANBERRIES

CURRANTS

BING CHERRY

good meals taste better.

CURRANTS. Select firm, ripe currants for jelly-making. Over-ripe fruit does not "jell" so well. The three main varieties are red, white and black, and are in season June to August.

ELDERBERRIES. Small black berries of the elder bush, principally used in jelly and wine-making, pies and breads.

GOOSEBERRIES. Approximately 50 species are distributed over the Northern Hemisphere, with the greatest number in North America. They have been cultivated in home gardens in the Low Countries of Europe from the beginning of the 16th Century. The English get a great deal of enjoyment from the ripened gooseberry, but the American taste tends toward the fully-developed but unripened fruit.

Federal and State laws regulate interstate shipments of gooseberries and the areas in which they may be grown, since this plant acts as a host to a fungus that attacks the white pine, one of the most valuable trees in this country. When available through local supplies or on farmers markets, fresh gooseberries are in season May through August, with June and July as peak months. Ripe gooseberries are easy to recognize: they are soft, have a light amber color, with the large ones being generally of preferred quality. Very high in Vitamin A and potassium, and a good amount of Vitamin C, phosphorus and calcium.

RASPBERRIES. The first *red* raspberries were introduced into cultivation in Europe about 400 years ago, and these European berries were introduced into the U. S. before 1800. The first *black* raspberries were probably introduced around 1850. The wild *red* raspberry is native of the Northern States, while the *black* is native farther South.

There are yellow or golden and apricot or amber-colored berries, as well as black, red, purple and various shades in between.

Raspberries are on the market from mid-April through November, with peak months of June and July.

Red raspberries contain 57 calories per 100 grams, while *black* contain 73 calories in the same amount. *Red* are high in Vitamin A, while *black* have only a trace. Both contain a good amount of Vitamin C, calcium, potassium and phosphorus.

STRAWBERRIES. The settlers going ashore in Massachusetts regaled themselves with a species of strawberries which abounded along the Eastern Seaboard and in the Northeastern part of the continent. The Indians were actually cultivating strawberries in 1643. It is believed that our modern strawberry is a descendant of the Chilean strawberry.

The strawberry is indigenous to many climates and soils and wherever it grows, it is in great abundance. Previous to World War II, California was a minor factor, supplying its own needs principally. With the resettlement of workers and production centers, the industry in California took on new life and is now the leading producer.

Large strawberries are the choicest for eating, although this is not a true sign that it may be the sweetest. Today, strawberry season is all year around — being available from some area in the U.S. every month of the year. Peak production, low prices, would generally prevail between mid-April and mid-July. Strawberries are low in calories, usually very high in Vitamin C and other minerals.

Here are two good tips to remember about berries: first, keep in mind that only the popular strawberry is privileged to wear a cap as a sign of maturity. All other berries that are mature should be free of their hull. Second, for best quality and taste, select those berries that are firm, plump and full-colored for the variety.

Learn to distinguish the different types: red and black raspberries (the core separates from the fruit); blackberries and dewberries . . . much alike and used the same way; loganberries . . . big, dark red berries from the Far West; and boysenberries, which greatly resemble them. Large-size blueberries are preferred to smaller ones as they have a better flavor. The cultivated blueberry in today's retail store is distinctly different from the wild huckleberry, the latter having ten large seeds that crackle as the berry is eaten.

For practically every member of the berry family, optimum storage conditions are 32° F. and 90% relative humidity. Plan to use them quickly, as they have a short life! (See "cranberries" for excepted handling recommendations.)

Eaten raw, it is one of the important detergent fruits helpful to dental health.

Blackberries, blueberries, strawberries, for instance, spell good eating for cereals, ideal for tarts, pies and salads, milk shakes. Should the fruit become soft, mash them and cook briefly in a simple sugar syrup. This makes a delicious ice cream topping or sauce for day-old cake. Even cranberries lend themselves to a delicious pie, jellied salads, upside-down cakes, muffins.

Practically all "berries" mentioned in this section are covered by a U.S.D.A. grade specification, generally U.S. No. 1 or better. There are so many variables in color, size and general appearance, they are seldom sold by grade. Few know blueberry size, for instance, is based on count in a half-pint basket: 90 or less, 90 to 130, 130 to 190, and 190 or more are acceptable specifications.

CHERRIES

The earliest history of cherry culture is lost in antiquity. The domestication of cherries probably began in China, whose agriculture dates back about 4,000 years. Cherries from Europe were introduced in America as soon as the English, French and Dutch were established. Cherries were in cultivation in Massachusetts in 1629, only nine years after the Pilgrims landed.

The two principal varieties of sweet cherries grown for fresh market are Bing and Lambert. The Bing matures before the Lambert in all districts and is characterized by its large size and round, plump shape, plus the dark "mahogany" color. It is the most popular of the fresh market varieties and is primarily grown in the Western areas that have just the right climatic conditions for this variety. It is an excellent "shipper".

The Lambert is similar to the Bing in many ways. It matures a week to ten days *after* the Bing and is grown in the same producing areas. It has the same rich flavor as the Bing, but is more elongated or heart-shaped. The Lambert variety is also hardy.

A third, and newer, variety of sweet cherries, the Van, has gained favor among the fresh buying trade. It is used as a pollenizer for Bings and has many of the same characteristics. Except for a somewhat shorter stem, it is difficult to distinguish it from the Bing, maturing about one week later.

The Chinook variety is an early black, sweet cherry of good size that is used as a pollenizer for Bings. It matures just ahead of the Bing, is very flavorful, slightly softer than the Bing and is not considered an ideal shipping variety.

Black Tartarian, Burbank, Chapman and Burlat are varieties that are grown in California, primarily because of their early-maturing characteristics. Although there are quality variances between these varieties, they generally are all dark red, soft, mostly small size, and are considered to be of fair quality.

The Black Republican variety is considered an excellent pollenizer in the Northwest, but is seldom shipped fresh market. Size generally quite small. It is very firm, but the quality is just fair. Black Republicans mature during the Lambert season.

Royal Ann and Rainier (Golden Bing) are both light or white sweet cherries. They gain excellent size, have outstanding flavor, but are very poor shippers. The light skin emphasizes even the slightest bruising, which detracts from the appearance of these varieties at retail. They mature about one week before Bings.

Schmidt and Windsor are Eastern sweet cherry varieties and both are grown mainly as processing varieties. They are dark, sweet cherries, characterized by good size and a quite firm, meaty texture. They are considered good for canning and brining.

The most widely-used shipping containers for sweet cherries from the Pacific Coast are wooden or corrugated lugs.

The fruit is available from May through July. Optimum storage conditions for the fruit are 32° F. and 90% relative humidity.

Eaten raw, it is one of the important detergent fruits helpful to dental health.

Cherries are so delicate that they must be handled carefully to avoid bruising or other damage. Prime quality fruit should appear fresh, firm, well matured and well colored for the variety; be juicy and of fine flavor. Use the taste test.

TART CHERRY VARIETIES. Early Richmond is mainly grown in the Middle West and East. It matures in early June, is dark red, round, medium to large, juicy and considered good for canning only.

English Morello, again, is mainly a Middle West and Eastern variety. It is harvested around July 15, is dark red, medium to large, juicy and considered good for canning only.

Montmorency is grown in all sections. Harvested in July, is light to dark red, medium to large, and juicy. It is the most popular of the sour cherry varieties and may be eaten fresh.

Principal uses of cherries are eating out-of-hand, in salads, cooked in pies, tarts, cakes, jellies, jams, preserves, sauces, pickles and candies. They are used in ice cream, puddings and other desserts, as well as fruit cups.

For those of you who have found it a task to pit cherries, the use of a clean pen holder with a strong point inserted in it is suggested. You'll need a quick, handy tool for pitting if you're going to make full use of this delicious fruit.

Per pound fresh weight, cherries contain 261 calories, 4.7 grams protein, 2.1 grams fat, 63.2 grams carbohydrates, 77 mg. calcium, 85 mg. phosphorus, 1.7 mg. iron and 2,830 I. U. of Vitamin A.

Cherry sizes are described in *"rows"*, dating back to when the industry place-packed the top layer in the box. A tight fit of ten cherries across the narrow face of the lug became "10 row" cherries. Depending on variety, 9-row is generally the very largest packed, 13-row the smallest. But a 10-row California cherry is smaller than a 10-row shipped from Washington, for example — just to keep you thoroughly confused. Reason: California ships an 18 lb. net lug, Washington a larger, 20 lb. lug.

CHERRY VARIETIES AND HARVEST PERIODS BY AREAS OF PRODUCTION

(Beginning and completion dates for harvest may vary from 7-10 days, depending on preharvest temperatures)

GROWING AREAS	Tartarian, Burlats, Chapman, Burbank	Bing	Lambert, Van Black Republican	Royal Ann, Golden Bing, Schmidt, Windsor
CALIFORNIA SAN JOAQUIN SANTA CLARA	5/5 - 5/20	5/18 - 6/6 6/1 - 6/15	5/25 - 6/10 6/8 - 6/19	
OREGON MILTON-FREEWATER MID-COLUMBIA		6/12 - 6/26 6/15 - 7/10	6/25 - 7/20	
WASHINGTON YAKIMA WENATCHEE		6/12 - 7/10 6/15 - 7/24	6/26 - 7/12 7/6 - 8/3	
IDAHO CALDWELL EMMETT		6/26 - 7/10	7/6 - 7/15	
UTAH		7/6 - 7/18	7/10 - 7/20	
MIDWEST & EAST				7/12 - 7/20

TART CHERRY VARIETIES

	Early Richmond	English Morello	Montmorency
NORTHWEST **MIDWEST** **EAST**	Early June	Mid-June	July July July

COCONUTS

The coconut palm is probably native to the Malay Archipelago and possibly to Tropical America. The coconut tree matures at seven years and produces nuts for 70 or 80 years. There is a saying that "he who plants a coconut tree, plants vessels and clothing, food and drink, a habitation for himself and a heritage for his children." The fruit, botanically, is not a nut but a drupe.

The person who buys a coconut for the first time wants to know how to get at the meat and milk. There are three soft spots at the top of the shell. Pierce these with an ice pick, or similar sharp instrument, drain the milk; then tap all over with a hammer until the hard shell cracks and falls off. Another way to break off the shell is to heat the coconut in the oven for 30 minutes at 350° F.

Coconuts are on the market all year with peak availability in October, November and December. Good quality coconuts are those which are heavy for their size and in which the milk sloshes around. Coconuts without milk are spoiled. Nuts with moldy or wet "eyes" are unsound.

They are best stored at 32°-35° F., relative humidity of 90%. Under these conditions, they can be held for one or two months. The dry kernel, or meat, is the copra of commerce from which coconut oil is expressed. The meat of the coconut may be eaten by hand, without further preparation, or substituted for dried, packaged coconut in recipes.

Nutritionally, the main value of coconut meat is caloric, containing 346 calories per 100 grams.

Hundreds of millions of people in tropical and subtropical countries use coconuts daily, world production being 26-29 billion nuts a year!

DATES

Known as the "candy that grows on trees", dates were cultivated in modern Iraq as far back as 3500 B.C. The date was first introduced into the Western world by early Spanish missionaries. Some of the original palms, or their offshoots, are still found in parts of Southern California and Mexico.

The leading producing states are California and Arizona. They are also found in Texas, Florida and Gulf States, but in these regions climatic conditions seldom permit the fruit to ripen properly.

There are more than 100 varieties of dates grown in the Coachella Valley of Southern California. It is the

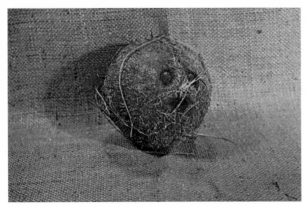

REGULAR COCONUT

COCONUT, IN HUSK

DATES

BLACK MISSION

KING

KADOTA

RUBY RED

WHITE MARSH

only area in the Western Hemisphere where dates are grown on a commercial basis.

Dates are classified as "soft", "semi-dry" and "dry" depending upon the softness of the ripe fruit. Another classification is according to the kind of sugar contained in the ripe fruit, with most *soft* varieties being invert-sugar dates and most *dry* varieties cane-sugar dates.

The principal commercial variety in the U.S. is the Deglet Noor, meaning "Date of the Light". It is a semi-dry variety, an excellent eating date, has high cane sugar content and ripens late in the season. Commercially, it accounts for about 85% of the total date acreage. It is the only semi-dry variety that is a cane sugar date; the others are invert sugar varieties.

The Halaway, Khadrawy and Zahidi varieties are invert sugar dates. The Khadrawy is a soft variety, while Halaway and Zahidi are semi-dry. These varieties are in great demand by the people who must guard their sugar intake. This is a natural sugar (like honey) and is composed of dextrose and levulose.

When fully ripe, fresh dates are plump and lustrous with a golden brown color and smooth skin. They are sold pitted and unpitted and are available throughout the year. The season of top abundance is from September to May, with the peak in November.

Dates will keep indefinitely if properly cared for and stored. Like any delicately-flavored fruit, certain precautions must be taken to insure keeping the dates in prime condition. Ideal storage conditions are between 30° and 40° F., relative humidity of 75-80%. The lower the temperature, the longer the fruit will retain its original quality. Dates should not be stored near flour or cereal or any other items that might be infested. Do not store near onions, fish or other odorous items, for dates tend to absorb such odors.

Delicious when eaten fresh, dates are an excellent addition to many dishes. They are especially delectable with the morning cereal or tossed in with other fruits in salads. Dates add fruity quality to muffins, cookies and salads — as well as being a moisture retaining factor.

They are a fair source of Vitamins A and B, protein, calcium and phosphorus. Dates are an unusually good source of iron. They are also a good source of copper, and contain small amounts of other essential minerals. Being 60-65% sugars, athletes use dates as a quick energy food — 100 grams edible portion provide 274 calories of food energy.

Dry varieties usually contain only a small amount of moisture when ripe and are non-perishable; the soft and semi-dry varieties contain a considerable amount of moisture and are usually highly perishable.

FIGS

The fig tree was probably first cultivated in the fertile part of southern Arabia. Discovery of fossil figs in deposits of France and Italy testify to the ancient origin of this species. Figs were growing before recorded history, Stone Age. In the Bible, the significance of the fig began with the story of the Garden of Eden. Figs were well-known in Egypt, 2000 B.C., as shown in their drawings and tombs.

Figs were introduced into America by the Spaniards and throughout Hispaniola in 1520. In California, the fig dates back to the first mission established at San Diego in 1769 and the variety planted there was named Mission, the leading black fig grown in California today.

The commercial fig is not a fruit in the strict botanical sense, but a hollow, fleshy receptacle with the many true fruits or "seeds" on the inside of it, and an opening at the top through which passes the insect that pollinates the minute fruit.

California produces the largest volume of figs, both Mission (or Adriatic) and the Smyrna types. The latter requires special provision for pollination by a gall wasp. In Texas and the Eastern States, only the Adriatic type is grown, which requires no pollination to set fruit.

There are many varieties of figs, but they are classified by shape, color of skin and color of flesh. The shape is round or turbinate in some, pyriform or obovate in others.

Smyrna is the common imported dried fig of commerce which is produced in considerable quantities in California. This variety does not develop its fruit to maturity, as a rule, except when it is pollinated by a certain fig wasp, known as a Blastophaga, which lives over the winter in a caprifig. (Caprifigs produce pollen, but their fruit is of little or no value for edible purposes.)

The Celeste is the variety very largely grown throughout all but the Texas portion of the Fig Belt. In the Gulf Coast region of Texas, the *Magnolia* is of similar, or perhaps even greater, relative importance than the Celeste is elsewhere.

Figs grown in the humid regions of the South Atlantic Coastal Plain and the Gulf Regions are extremely perishable, will ferment and sour under ordinary conditions within a comparatively short time after they are picked. Prompt utilization of the fruit, as it ripens, is imperative. (All figs will spoil more quickly in damp, muggy, rainy weather than in bright, clear weather.)

Figs can be grown in most climates, but in the more arid areas of California, the fruit can be left on the tree without deterioration until it is ripe enough to drop of its own accord, but for fresh shipment and use, they are *never* allowed to drop.

Black Mission. When fully ripe, skin is almost black — good for eating out of hand, stewing or for pies and cakes.

Brown Turkey (or Brown Naples or Blue Burgundy). Medium to large, short, pear-shaped with a thick stalk, brownish-purple with bluish bloom; red flesh, juicy and richly flavored.

Brunswick. Fruit very large, broad, pear-shaped with short, rather slender stalk; ribs well marked; skin tough, dark brown in color; pulp thick, pink, soft; quality fair. Mid-season and late.

Calimyrna. Generally large, has a greenish-yellow skin and very sweet, somewhat nut-like flavor. Ideal for hand-eating.

Celeste. Small to medium in size, pear-shaped, ribbed, violet color; sometimes shaded purplish-brown; stems short, stout; flesh white, shading to rose-color at center, firm, juicy, sweet, excellent quality. One of the hardiest varieties of figs and can be grown far outside the usual limits of culture. Season early. Very desirable for canning and preserving.

Kadota. Known as the *Dottato* in some countries. Large, green or yellowish-green, pear-shaped with a thick neck. Flesh is violet-tinted, juicy and excellent quality.

Optimum storage is at 32° F. and 90% relative humidity — but it is best to plan on eating immediately! Ripeness can be ascertained by the degree of softness to the touch, while over-ripeness is detected by a sour odor, due to fermentation of the juice.

Figs are a good source of natural fruit sugar with a calorie rating that is not too high. Fresh figs are especially suited for hand eating and as a garnish in salads; to top fresh fruit cups and compotes. They are palatable and healthful sweeteners, as well as being easily digested. They are popular in salads, cakes and candies.

Nutritionally, *raw*, naturally ripe figs, per 100 grams of edible portion, provide the following: water 78%, calories 79-88, protein 1.4 gm., calcium 54 mg., phosphorus, iron, Vitamin A (90 I.U.), Vitamin C 2 mg. *Dried:* 300 calories per 100 grams of edible portion; protein 2.0 gm., calcium 223 mg., phosphorus 104 mg., Vitamin A 125 I.U.

Pickers of fresh figs usually wear cotton gloves as protection against acrid fig juice, carry hooked sticks to pull down branches, either twist the neck of the fig, or, sometimes, cut it from the tree with a knife. Most fruits are picked mature-green for shipping, but the fig must be tree-ripened to reach its full sugar content and provide proper eating quality.

GRAPEFRUIT

While the world grapefruit production has increased appreciably the past several years, the U. S. continues the leading producer with an average of seven times more than Israel. Other sizeable producing countries are Argentina, Republic of South Africa and Cyprus.

If you are like most people, having red, rough-looking skin around your elbows, you may be tempted to rest each elbow in a grapefruit half during your moments of relaxation! While this may sound strictly "kooky" to you, this little beauty hint is passed along by the Florida Department of Citrus to correct the elbow-skin problem experienced by most people. (Citrus is an excellent astringent.)

Grapefruit, occasionally referred to as the "Shaddock" or "pomelo", has been a native of North America since its importation by the old Spanish settlers. How this name originated is still a moot question, but it is generally attributed to the fact that the fruit grows in clusters like grapes.

But no matter the name by which you call this tart-sweet citrus fruit, it has won itself a preferred position in countless homes. Due to its tangy, exhilarating flavor, and because it is one of the best sources of that all-important Vitamin C, grapefruit is a breakfast favorite during its year-round season. An 8-ounce glass of freshly squeezed juice will supply more than the average daily requirement of ascorbic acid (Vitamin C). Not to be overlooked, too, by anyone on a reducing diet, is the fact that grapefruit is a low-calorie food and highly alkalizing in nature. Eaten raw, it is one of the important detergent fruits helpful to dental health.

Keep in mind, to secure the greatest nutritional benefit of grapefruit, plan on eating the whole segment. In mature fruit, with knife or fingernail, it is no more difficult to segment a grapefruit than it is an orange!

But, to get on to the shopping points, no doubt you have found that two grapefruit of the same size will often vary in taste and juiciness. The one will be heavy, firm and smoothly textured, with a well-rounded shape, or flattened — a good indication of fine, juicy grapefruit. The other will be coarse, puffy and rough — indicative of lack of juice, as well as taste. Since grapefruit is, on the average, over three-quarters liquid, heaviness is a good indication of juice content.

Do not rely solely on color for an index to flavor, as good grapefruit can range from pale yellow to russet or bronze. Brightly colored fruit is naturally more appealing — yet a russeted fruit may often be tastier and juicier. Minor surface blemishes do not affect the eating quality, although the presence of a bad bruise may indicate some internal breakdown, which is not apparent on the outside.

Skin color does not indicate ripeness. As in all citrus, a grapefruit tree may have blossoms, immature fruit and ripe fruit on it all at the same time. In the spring, extra chlorophyll produced for new bloom tinges the already ripened fruit with green color. This natural process is called "regreening" and in no way affects the quality. Grapefruit is *never* artificially colored.

Florida and Texas are the principal producing States between the months of September and June, supplemented between January and June by grapefruit growing in the deserts of Arizona and California. Summer grapefruit originates principally in California. The two main types are the Duncan, containing numerous seeds, and the Marsh seedless which has very few seeds. The pink-meated grapefruit, relatively a newcomer in the citrus realm, is a cross-bred creation, and many people consider the "pink-meats" somewhat sweeter than others. These popular varieties are known as Foster Pinks, Thompson Pinks or Marsh Pinks, Ruby Reds — the latter two varieties being relatively seedless.

For purely psychological reasons, the favorite of most consumers is the Ruby Red grapefruit, because of its "eye" appeal. The variety is one of nature's million dollar mistakes! It was discovered as a bud mutation on a Thompson pink tree, horticulturists grafting bud wood to several orange rootstocks, thus propagating what we know now as the "Ruby Red" grapefruit. It is the primary grapefruit grown in Texas, is also grown in large quantities in Florida.

Today, the Star Ruby is a new strain developed in Texas and is reputed to have a much deeper red than the Ruby Red, is sweeter and yet has a higher acid content; also, it is supposed to hold its color later in the season and have a reddish-gold peel color that could be extraordinary.

The Indian River area of Florida, a narrow strip of land along the East Coast of the State, stretching from Daytona on the north to West Palm Beach on the South, has long been noted for its production of top quality citrus. About 50% of the State's huge fresh-marketed grapefruit crop is grown in the area and has been the backbone of the area's citrus production; orange and various mandarin tree plantings have increased dramatically in recent years.

Little known even in the industry is the basic size-of-fruit difference between Florida and "other" grapefruit. Since this fruit, like many others, is sized and sold by count per half-box carton, the larger-sized carton used in Florida makes their fruit, size for size, about one size larger than the same count-size fruit

from Texas, California or Arizona!

In the home, grapefruit should be held at 50° F. and 85% relative humidity.

The Shaddock is named for the man who brought it to Barbados sometime prior to 1707; also called "pomelo". Largest of the citrus fruit, resembles an enlarged and elongated grapefruit, can weigh as much as 15-20 pounds. Fruit very coarse, thick peel and coarse-grained, bitter-acid flesh; juice scanty. Perhaps the parent of today's cultivated grapefruit, it originated in China, now grown in all or most of the warmer citrus districts where its large foliage makes it an interesting garden plant. It is of no commercial importance in North America.

As a concluding thought about grapefruit, remember this: whichever kind you purchase, look for the name "Blue Goose" stamped on the skin. It is placed there for your protection to give you the best in value for the money you spend. This nationally-famous trademark identifies "the best of the better crops".

GRAPES

The people of Biblical times were perhaps more familiar with grapes, their culture and uses, than we are today. In the hot, Asiatic countries, as in many European nations, wines made principally from the juice of grapes were frequently drunk in place of water. Unsanitary conditions and lack of pure drinking water contributed largely to the prevalence of this custom.

In any event, grapes have been a popular fruit down through the centuries and are raised in large quantities in the U.S. Actually, the grape is grown over the greater part of the world except in regions of extreme cold. Grape-growing is the world's biggest fruit industry!

Grapes for commercial use are divided into four major, one minor group: table, raisin, wine, juice, with canning the minor group. The same grape may be in more than one, or even in all, groups, such as the Thompson Seedless, which is suitable for all five types of uses. A limited number of varieties produce wines of good quality — and raisins, for example, are produced mainly from three varieties.

Table grapes are those intended for use as fresh fruit, either for food or decorative purposes. Fewer than a dozen varieties are grown extensively for table grapes.

When selecting grapes, choose those bunches that are well formed and good looking. You will find color is a good guide to ripeness. The darker varieties should be free of a green tinge, while white grapes should have a decided amber coloring when completely matured.

ALMERIA

CALMERIA

CARDINAL, GIBBED—UNGIBBED

CONCORD

EMPEROR

ITALIA MUSCAT

LADY FINGER

PERLETTE

THOMPSON SEEDLESS, UNGIBBED

TOKAY

Fully ripened grapes are fairly soft to the touch and tender to the taste.

Unlike some other fruit, grapes *will not improve* in either color, sugar, nor quality, after they have been harvested and, therefore, should not be expected to ripen, having left the vine.

California produces about 90% of the table and juice grapes, all of the European (Vitis vinifera) species. Tables grapes are available from early June through April or May. The Eastern States produce the Vitis labrusca (American type) species and these grapes are available in the fall months only.

You will find that the skin of a California grape adheres tightly to the pulp, but its seeds are easily removed. This, however, is just the opposite of the Eastern grape, for the skin of the latter separates from the pulp easily while its seeds are difficult to pry away from the meat.

Generally speaking, the Western varieties are the sweeter of the two, although Eastern varieties are eaten out of hand just as much as they are made into jellies, wines or grape juices.

In California, Perlettes, Thompson Seedless and Beauty Seedless are sprayed with a gibberellin material to increase berry size for table use. Gibberellin is a pre-bloom treatment to lengthen stems, increase berry size. The method of application is in a water spray with a wetting agent. In effect, the material delays maturity in proportion to the increase in berry size. In a very general way, berry size is increased 28% in Thompson Seedless; in Beauty Seedless, gibberellin-treated grapes increase an average of 46%. It helps to produce large, oval-shaped berries with firm flesh, mild in taste, with a sweet, fine flavor.

Listed below (alphabetically, not in order of importance) are the most important varieties:

ALMERIA. A yellow-green, fairly sweet white grape, slight Muscat flavor.

CALMERIA. Large, elongated berry with firm pulp. Green-white color with fairly thick skin. Mild in flavor.

CARDINAL. Handsome dark-red berries that may attain an inch or more in diameter. Clusters are long and conical. Mild tasting, delicious.

CATAWBA. Large, purplish-red, distinctive flavor. Sometimes a table grape, but mostly used for wine and juice. Best storing of the American type.

CONCORD. Blue; the standard Eastern variety, unexcelled for grape juice, jelly or table use. Now the principal American-type grape.

DELAWARE. Small, pink, tender skin. Used as table grape and for wine.

EMPEROR. Red; the latest maturing California variety; large, red festive berries with a cherry flavor. Clusters are large and very full.

EXOTIC. Large, black berry, clusters are long, full and handsome. Flesh is crisp, taste is subtle.

FLAME TOKAY. Red; large, round berries, medium to large bunches.

LADY FINGER. A pale green, large, very elongated white grape.

MALAGA. White Malaga, medium-size bunches, round-white, medium-size berries; Red Malaga, larger, round-red berries.

MUSCAT. A greenish-yellow, oval-white grape, used for wine.

NIAGARA. Large, amber with heavy gray bloom, medium sugar content, coarse and rather sour flavor.

PERLETTES. A white, rather small, round to olive-shaped berries, fairly small to medium-sized bunches, rather compact, tight bunches. The earliest maturing California variety, seedless.

RIBIER. Black; large, round berries, small to large bunches.

THOMPSON SEEDLESS. White; small, olive-shaped berries, sweet and seedless.

The earliest maturing California grapes are Perlettes,

available the first week in June. Cardinals start shipping in mid-June, followed by Thompson Seedless, which leads all other varieties in quantity produced. Ribiers start to market in August; Tokays in September; Emperors in October. Emperor is the main storage fresh grape available throughout the winter and into April or May.

Thompson Seedless is probably the most useful grape in the home, since it requires next to no labor to use. For hand eating or use in pies, tarts, salads; dark grapes offer interesting color, flavor and texture contrast to fruit cups and salads. When preparing any grapes for garnishing in small clusters, cut the clusters with scissors, which helps keep the grapes united to the stem.

Grapes are highly perishable, so handle them carefully. They should be refrigerated near 32° F., 90% relative humidity. Use them quickly, while they are at their very best!

One-half cup of Thompson Seedless (60 medium-size grapes) provides only 66 calories, low in sodium, and contains some amounts of other vital nutritional elements.

LEMONS

It took the California Gold Rush of 1849 to establish the commercial lemon industry. The miners who flocked to the Golden State were ten times the State's previous population. Food was scarce and high-priced. The inevitable scurvy (due to shortage of Vitamin C in the diet) became rampant in the mining camps. Since lemons are a sure cure for scurvy, miners were willing to pay a dollar apiece for lemons and oranges. More lemon trees were planted to meet the demands. By 1856, a new industry was born.

The U. S. and Italy are the world's main producers of lemons, each with a production of 15-17 million boxes, out of a total of approximately 50 million. Other large producers are Greece, Spain, Argentina and Chile — in that order of major production.

Lemons are available all year in adequate quantities to meet the demand. In general, there are two types — the acid and the sweet — with the latter type grown as a novelty.

Virtually all lemons are shipped to market in the ½ box corrugated carton, approximately 38 lbs. net weight. Instead of hand, place-packing of lemons, for several years most cartons have been "volume filled", with conveyors dropping the fruit through an automatic counting device and into the carton. The lemons, being an irregularly shaped object, are vibrated into layers of fruit in the carton, a special vibrator below

the carton as it is dump-filled.

Most lemons are sorted and re-sorted throughout the season to secure proper color and maturity. An expensive "electric eye" machine has been developed to separate yellow, silver, light green or dark green at the rate of 40 fruit per second, with high accuracy, but most color separating is still done by the experienced "naked eye". Similar to a terminal market tomato ripening-packing operation, as lemons are graded, the too-green are separated back into field boxes or bins, sent to "curing rooms", are eventually withdrawn at a later date and again color-graded.

Here's what to look for in buying lemons. The best have a fine-textured skin and are heavy for their size. Those that are coarse skinned, or light in weight, have less juice. The fruit that has a slightly greenish cast is likely to have more acid than that which is deep yellow. Deep yellow lemons are usually more mature than light yellow, and not quite as acid.

Under ideal storage conditions, 58-60° F. and 89-91% relative humidity, a U.S.D.A. test revealed lemons lost weight at the rate of only 2-3% a month; that juice content of the individual lemons increased after 1-2 months in storage; acid yield increased the first month. And finally, ascorbic acid concentration remained nearly constant throughout seven months' storage. (One medium size fruit provides 55% of the recommended daily allowance of this vitamin.)

Buy according to the size wanted for the particular use. Medium lemons are considered all-purpose fruit for sectioning, juicing.

Of all the members of the citrus family, lemons undoubtedly have more uses that are out of the ordinary than any of the others.

Since lemons, like all citrus, are composed largely of water, they tend to shrivel after being kept for a long time. Immersing them in hot water for half an hour, or longer, helps to restore their freshness and will increase appreciably the amount of juice which can be extracted.

The lemon has flavor power. It sharpens sweet, perks up the bland, and enlivens the pallid.

With the popularity of iced tea and seafood in today's meals, fresh lemons add zest to these refreshers. Lemon pies, tarts, cakes and cookies are highly popular. The lemon plays an important role in special diets, too. When salt is restricted, a drop or two of lemon juice add piquancy and flavor to otherwise bland food. Lemon is frequently used to replace oil in dressings by those seeking to reduce their weight. The juice will accent the flavor of soups and juices, such as tomato juice.

LEMONS

PERSIAN LIMES

HAWAIIAN LIMES

Arizona and California today represent practically all U. S. production, with Ventura County of California producing four times more than the Arizona and California desert districts, almost 20 times as much as Northern and Central California; however, today there is more new, non-bearing acreage in the ground in districts other than Ventura, than presently in production, indicating a more equal production among the three districts for the future.

It has long been recognized that Florida and Texas can grow lemons, and during the past few years, new plantings in Florida have increased appreciably, indicating sizeable fresh and processed marketing for the future. Texas production will be quite limited for some time.

Little-known to many in lemon marketing is the comparatively small fresh, domestic lemon consumption. From Arizona-California growings, recent years, only 35-40% of total grown is marketed fresh through domestic channels; 18-20% is exported and another 41-47% is put into products or other diversion.

Nutritionally, 100 grams edible portion of peeled fruit contains 27 calories, some protein, calcium, phosphorus, potassium, Vitamin A, in addition to ascorbic acid.

LIMES

Limes are native to India. They subsequently spread to the Asiatic mainland and are now grown in many other tropical and subtropical regions of the world. It seems likely that Columbus brought seeds of limes to the New World on his second voyage in 1493. Limes were probably introduced to Florida in the 1500's, and to California during the period of the establishment of the missions, about 1769.

Only acid type limes are grown in the U. S., while sweet limes are popular in many other citrus growing areas. Acid limes are further divided into Tahiti (large fruits) and Mexican (small fruits with thin rinds) types.

Varieties of the Tahiti type include *Persian* (called Tahiti in California), *Bearss, Idemore* and *Pond*. The Persian variety is the most extensively grown commercially. It was introduced from Algeria into Florida in 1898. Its outstanding characteristics include large size, fine grained pulp, light greenish-yellow color, very acid and highly flavored. Fruit color, when fully ripe, is light orange-yellow (marketed at green mature stage). Fruit matures the year around.

REGULAR TANGERINE

MINNEOLA TANGELO

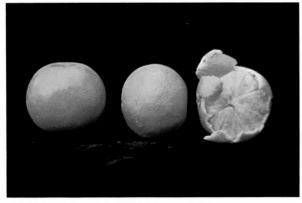

REGULAR TANGELO

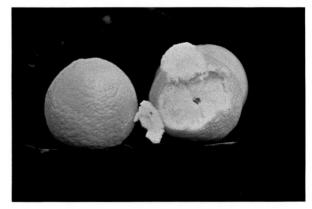

ALGERIAN TANGERINE

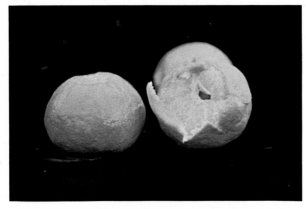

DANCY TANGERINE

TEMPLE ORANGE

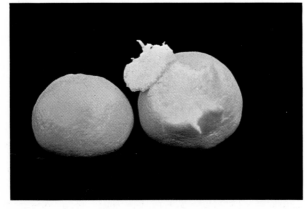

KINNOW MANDARIN

KUMQUATS

38

The Bearss is the principal lime variety in California. It is distinguished from the Persian by its smaller fruit, very juicy pulp. It is very acid, of excellent quality, with no seeds. Fruit color, when fully ripe, is light lemon-yellow. Season is winter to late spring, with fruit maturing more or less throughout the year.

Under the Mexican Group is the Key lime of Florida, known as *Mexican* in the Southwestern U. S.; as *Dominican* when imported from the Dominican Republic, or *West Indian* when imported from any of the West Indies. Mexican limes are distinguished by light lemon-yellow color of fruit, round to oval shape, and small size. The rind is smooth, leathery, and very thin.

The juice is abundant, flavor strong and very acid. Season is late fall to spring, maturing more or less in some volume throughout the year. They are marketed when fully ripe.

With reference to Persian type limes, those that are green in color and heavy for their size are the most desirable.

Limes are a good source of Vitamin C; they contain 37 calories per 100 grams.

Fresh lime juice is used in the preparation of beverages, and is a natural base for fruit punches; or the juice alone may be used on salads. Lime juice is popular in sherbets, pies, and ice box cakes. Slices of fresh limes make attractive garnishes for meat and fish dishes, and as a "dress-up" for iced tea. Try some fresh lime juice on your next melon!

MANDARINS

If you have been frantically looking for a "tangerine" section in this book, you have been conforming to general consumer, and even industry, disagreement . . . knowingly or unknowingly. To most people in the U.S., the name "tangerine" applies to all zipper-skin (some call them slip-skin) citrus marketed; however, "tangerine" is the name for only one type of mandarin!

But *all* mandarins are easy to peel, making them a world-wide favorite for snacks, lunchbox, salads and picnics.

Mandarins botanically refer to three classifications of oranges: 1) Satsumas, 2) Tangerines, 3) Miscellaneous hybrids, which include the Tangelo (Orlando, Minneola, etc.); the Tangors (King, Murcott, Temple) and complex hybrids (Robinson, Lee, Page, etc.).

There are a multitude of tangerine varieties, and an even greater number of "complex hybrids". Throughout the U.S., retailers generally identify the varieties that are rather small, deep-orange colored, with a rather soft, short-necked, pebbly skin as "tangerines." "Tangelos" are generally identified this way . . . and some retailers add the "Orlando" or "Minneola".

We've never seen a retailer display a "Tangor" . . . they're generally identified separately as either "Murcott" (name recently changed to "Honey Tangerine") or "Temple".

confuse the consumer more than she is, whatever varieties in *this* group that look like the others, are identified at the point-of-sale accordingly.

A few retailers will identify "satsuma" as such . . . but they're generally called "tangerines".

When a whole mandarin is cut crosswise, it looks identical to an orange on the interior, the segments arranged in petal fashion, a small, pulpy core in the center. But when peeled, they immediately reveal their most distinctive feature: the segments separate easily into compact, taste-tickling sensations!

Florida is the largest producer of mandarins in the U.S., with California a poor second, followed by Arizona and Texas. They generally are first available in October, supplies ending in May, peak production in the November through January period.

Mexico has become a very large producer of various mandarin varieties, exports internationally and principally to Canada (duty free), and a good quantity to the U.S., much to the disgust of the latter's growers of the variety. Japan is the largest producer in the world of the true satsuma, exports a considerable quantity; and in Western Canada, it is considered a Christmas-season delight akin to candy canes in the U.S. During the 1970-71 marketing season, Japan was allowed to distribute a small quantity to five Northwestern States of the U. S.

The standard shipping container in Florida is a 4/5 bu. crate or carton. As in most fruits, size designation is by number, reflecting the count by container, dominant sizes being 176s and 210s, most crops.

Despite the urging of receivers, California and Arizona continue to designate their mandarin sizes with alleged word descriptions, having no reference to pieces of fruit per container:

Size Designation	Diameter Inches
Super Colossal	3.25-3.75
Colossal	3.00-3.25
Mammoth	2.75-3.00
Jumbo	2.50-2.75
Large	2.25-2.50
Medium	2.00-2.25
Small	1.75-2.00

Nutritional composition is available on *tangerines*, revealing an excellent source of vitamin C: one 2½" tangerine provides 37% of the daily recommended allowance for an adult. For each 3½ oz. edible portion, it has 46 calories, 420 I.U. of Vitamin A, 126 mg. of potassium; calcium, phosphorus and small amounts of practically all other minerals. Eaten raw, it is one of the important detergent fruits helpful to dental health.

The earliest recorded history of citrus dates back to 2200 B.C. in China. The name "Satsuma" is strictly Japanese. The "Tangerine" was introduced into Europe early in the 19th Century, and reached America the middle of that Century, when the Italian consul at New Orleans planted it on the consulate grounds. The root stock was brought to Florida some time between 1840 and 1893. It was Col. G. L. Dancy, an early Florida grower, who laughingly referred to the tangerine as a "kid-glove" orange . . . indicating it could easily be peeled without soiling your finest. The Colonel also gave his name to one of the best known, most popular varieties of the fruit.

For storage, temperatures of 38-40°F, relative humidity of 90-95% is considered ideal; during transport, same humidity, but 32-38°F.

In selecting fruit, it should be heavy for its size, indicating ample juice content, and have the characteristic deep orange, or almost red, color. A "puffy" appearance and "feel" is normal for many varieties, but it should still have the weight and there should be no soft, water-soaked areas or mold.

Mandarins are one of the most versatile fruits today . . . truly a convenience food! Many "fresh" industry leaders feel the mandarin-type fruits, with their zipper skins, hold greater marketing potential for the future than most orange varieties, because of the tremendous technological advances in processing orange juices.

Following is a brief description of some of the major mandarins:

CLEMENTINE (Algerian) MANDARIN. One of the earliest varieties to reach our markets. Generally called an Algerian tangerine. Fruit size is medium to large, and shape varies from slightly elongated to slightly flattened. The fruit has a red-orange, pebbled rind which peels easily. Seed number varies from none to many.

DANCY TANGERINE. Has a lively, sweet-tart flavor with many seeds in a loose, easy-to-peel rind. When the fruit becomes over-ripe, the rind looks dry and puffy.

FAIRCHILD TANGERINE. Principally grown in desert areas, generally medium to large size, slightly flat, smooth skin and deep orange color. Peels easily, many seeds, has a rich and sweet taste.

FORTUNE TANGERINE. Principally grown in desert areas, fruit slightly flat, red-orange color, slightly "lumpy" appearing with a tight rind sometimes difficult to peel. Many seeds, flavor brisk and sub-acid.

FREMONT TANGERINE. Grown desert areas, slightly flat, red-orange color and smooth skin easy to peel. Many seeds, a sprightly acid, but sweet, flavor.

KARA MANDARIN. A hybrid, it is a rather large mandarin with a pebbled to slightly rough, orange-colored rind. Fruit is deep oblate, usually with a small neck. Peels fairly well, has an attractive deep orange pulp, a medium number of seeds and excellent, rich flavor.

KINNOW. This is another hybrid Tangor whose trees are alternate bearers with consequent small fruit size in the heavy crop years. The fruit is slightly flattened with no neck and has a smooth, orange rind. The number of seeds is high and the segments do not separate easily. Fruit grown in the desert areas peel better than when grown elsewhere. It has a rich and sweet flavor with thin, tender membranes around the segments. Very heavy fruit for its size.

MINNEOLA TANGELO. This is actually a grapefruit-tangerine cross, but in all characteristics, it resembles the tangerine. Well-suited for growing in the desert areas, produces fruit of good size and appearance; red-orange and tends to be slightly elongated, often with some neck. Pulp is tender and fine-textured. Flavor fair to good with a grapefruit-like tartness.

MURCOTT (recently re-named "Honey Tangerine"). A Tangor fruit grown principally in Florida. Exceedingly sweet, rich, thin-skinned; fairly easily peeled. Like the Kinnow, very heavy for its size, very firm, extraordinarily good keeping qualities.

ORLANDO. This is a Tangelo and has the same parentage as the Minneola. Fruit is of medium size, slightly flattened and has an attractive, deep orange rind. Does not peel easily.

SATSUMA. This is the principal variety of Japan. Fruit size is medium to small. Fruit may be smooth and rather flattened but sometimes quite rough and necked. The rind is orange, pebbled and peels readily. Essentially seedless.

TEMPLE. No one knows the exact parentage but it is believed to be a cross between a tangerine and an orange. It is one of the finest quality citrus fruits grown in the U.S. but it has not done well in California. Generally of large size with a slightly rough-red-orange rind. Shape varies from spherical to slightly flattened. Generally firm and juicy with quite a few seeds. The flavor is distinct, rich and spicy, sweet-tart.

WILKING MANDARIN. This is a hybrid that has excellent flavor but the trees are extreme alternate bearing and in most areas have small fruit in heavy crop years. The fruit is firm, slightly flattened and without a neck. The rind is orange, fine-pebbled and peels fairly well. Flesh is deep orange, with a considerable number of seeds.

MELONS

Cantaloupes, or muskmelons, as they are sometimes called, were named after the city of Cantalupo where, according to some historians, this species of melon was first grown in Italy. Biologically, this name should apply only to one kind of muskmelon, that with a hard rind, and not the netted type so common in the U. S. But common usage has termed all muskmelons "cantaloupes." In reality, all the melons can trace their ancestry back to Asia, as do so many of our present-day fruits.

There is no absolutely sure guide for determining quality in melons from the outside, but some indicators are fairly dependable.

For cantaloupes, there should be no trace of a stem; there should be a very definite, pronounced cavity where the melon was pulled from the vine. If a cantaloupe is reasonably mature, the stem by which it was attached to the vine, will slip easily and completely away. Experienced produce men look for this "full slip" condition when making their purchases.

Also observe the netting and shape, for if the netting covers the cantaloupe thickly and stands out like a whipcord, the melon has another merit point. The background color under the netting should ideally be a slight golden, or, at worst, a light greenish-gray. (Avoid completely a dull, dark green background color.)

Ideally, it should be football shaped, or almost round, at worst. (Avoid lopsided or heavily indented melons.) It should have a delicate melon aroma. A slight rattling of the seeds, when shaken, is another sign of maturity; however, loose, watery seeds are, more than likely, the *first* sign of the *last* stages of maturity, and it *could* be slightly sour; or, it might be the finest 'lope you ever tasted!

Cantaloupes are produced commercially in 25 states and are grown in others for home consumption or local markets. California produces more cantaloupes than any other state.

Cantaloupes are available every month of the year, our earliest supplies originating in Mexico in January. June, July and August are the heaviest months of production in the U. S.

Plan to give cantaloupes two or three days at room temperature before serving. Time and warmth will not make it sweeter, but will soften the meat and make it juicier, two factors essential to melon appreciation.

Cantaloupes provide only 20 calories per 3½ oz. of edible portion, or 68 calories per pound of edible portion, plus good amounts of calcium, phosphorus, iron, potassium and is an excellent source of Vitamins A and C as well as magnesium.

Serve them in halves or wedges, or cut up the "meat" to use in fruit cups or salads — or make an attractive dessert or main dish with melon balls.

A fully mature honeydew should be creamy white or pale yellow, even on the underside. Fruit should be large, at least 6½"-7" in diameter, weighing about 5-7 lbs. Test the aroma, since a ripe honeydew has a distinct and pleasing fragrance. A very slight, oily film generally is noticeable on the outer rind, also.

Because large honeydew melons are "crown fruit" (those growing closest to root of the plant), these are generally the best eating quality and more "meaty". Seldom is a small honeydew really fine eating, nor does it have a thick meat.

Avoid completely honeydews with a noticeable greenish-white exterior, unless you are planning to use it for a centerpiece, for it will probably never ripen in your home.

Many retailers, recognizing most honeydews must be shipped in a hard condition, will pre-ripen the melons in banana-ripening rooms before offering to the public. If the melon you purchase is hard, but meets the size, weight and color requirements, let it stand in a warm room for several hours (or days), away from sunlight, preferably in high humidity, until the aroma and softness at the stem and blossom end appear. This is the only time you should then cut the melon for eating! Season of availability is May to November, generally.

Honeydews are a fair source of Vitamin C and can be eaten freely because of its low calorie content.

The honeyball is smaller than the honeydew and, instead of being smooth-surfaced, is covered with a thin but plainly visible netting. Honeyballs, when ripe, are slightly soft and fragrant; generally their flesh is a light white-green color, although some varieties are pink-meated. Season is June to November.

Among other melon varieties, you'll find the Casaba, large and round in shape, with a ridged and furrowed rind. It is golden yellow when ripe, with a white meat. The Santa Claus or Christmas melon looks like a small watermelon, but has the flesh of a honeydew. The Persian melon looks like a large flattened cantaloupe but has a yellow skin and netting and pink meat.

One of the finest eating melons is the Crenshaw; this is a hybrid variety of muskmelon. They generally weigh 7 to 9 pounds, are round at the base and come to a

CANTALOUPE

CASABA

CRENSHAW

HONEYDEW

PERSIAN

SANTA CLAUS

WATERMELON

42

point at the stem end. They have a gold and green rind, which is smooth, with no netting and a little ribbing. The meat is a bright salmon color; thick, juicy and very good when ripe.

As a general guide to selection of all of the above melons, the outer skin should be a good color and give off a rich aroma, slightly soft at the blossom end. Never cut any of these melons unless they are ripe — they do not ripen satisfactorily after cutting.

The essential factors of watermelon quality are maturity and size. The larger melons have more edible flesh, proportionately, than the smaller ones. If you are a watermelon "thumper" from way back, forget it! Thumping will get you nowhere.

Color is the best key to ripeness in watermelons. A yellowish underside, regardless of the rich green color of the rest of the melon, is a good sign of ripeness. A watermelon is somewhat like a book, in that you can't always tell its contents by its cover. When you go to buy a whole melon, look for one that is symmetrically shaped and has a velvety bloom — a dull, rather than a shiny surface. The underside should be turning from white or pale green to a light yellowish color.

Avoid "white heart" in watermelons — a hard, white streak running lengthwise through the melon. Seeds, too, give a clue to ripeness. If the melon is fully matured, the seeds are usually dark brown or black. (Only one variety, the Improved Garrisonian, has white seeds.)

Most retailers charge slightly more for cut watermelons. It is well worth it! In this way, you can see the maturity of the melon — the only *sure* way of selecting a *good* watermelon.

The watermelon's chief contribution is one of enjoyment — not a heavy quota of nutrients; however, watermelons do contribute a useful amount of Vitamin A and small amounts of other nutrients.

NECTARINES

"Nectarine" comes from the Greek "nekter"; in mythology, it is the "drink of the gods".

Historically, early nectarine varieties were small, fast-softening and white-fleshed — primarily adapted to the home and local markets. But the new and better varieties have peach "blood" in the crosses, in order to get large size and firmness. When peaches are brought into the breeding, however, all the first generation progeny come in as peaches and it is necessary to back-cross the breeding to get the one out of four nectarines in recessive segregation.

Thus, a nectarine is a nectarine — it is not a fuzzless peach, and it is not (as popularly believed), a cross between a peach and a plum. Like other stone fruits, including cherries and apricots, it is a member of the rose family and closely related to peaches and almonds.

It is one of the oldest of all fruits and apparently grew in China before the time of Christ.

While some Eastern States, and a few Southern, grow nectarines in small quantities, virtually all available in the market are grown in California, and the new varieties available today were developed since World War II.

We are illustrating here a chart of principal California varieties, together with their normal appearance on the market.

Like the peach, the nectarine does not gain sugar after harvest and if not well matured when picked, it will be unsatisfactory tasting. In addition to maturity, ideal storage conditions are 32° F. and 90% relative humidity, will keep the product in ideal condition for short periods of time.

Many horticulturists in the world predict that by the turn of the Century, Queen Peach will be replaced by the more prolific nectarine, which has greater eye-appeal at the retail level.

Newer nectarine varieties are large sized, bright red in color and usually yellow fleshed freestones. Since most new varieties of nectarines have full, red color *before* they are mature, color is not a good maturity index. The development of flesh color and rounding out of the fruit, is a much better criteria of maturity. Bright-looking, plump fruit with an orange-yellow color between the red areas, firm to moderately hard, will probably ripen normally within 2-3 days at room temperature. Avoid hard, dull fruit, or slightly shriveled and hard, for it was probably immature when picked. Avoid those with cracked or punctured skin or bruising. Russeting or staining of the skin may detract from appearance, but should have no effect on eating quality.

Nectarines provide a valuable amount of Vitamin A. One piece, 2½ x 2″ in diameter (114 grams), with about 100 grams edible portion, provides about a third of the recommended daily allowance of Vitamin A and a fifth of the Vitamin C. They are low in calories and sodium, thus are suitable in reducing diets or low sodium diets.

The nectarine can be used in any recipe that calls for peaches: eat them out of hand, use in compotes alone or with a variety of other fruits; in salads of many kinds, or a garnish with meat or poultry. An ideal cereal topping, or sliced and topped with milk or ice cream. Shortcake, frozen desserts, parfaits; in tarts, puddings — or a nectarine pie!

Eaten raw, it is one of the important detergent fruits helpful to dental health.

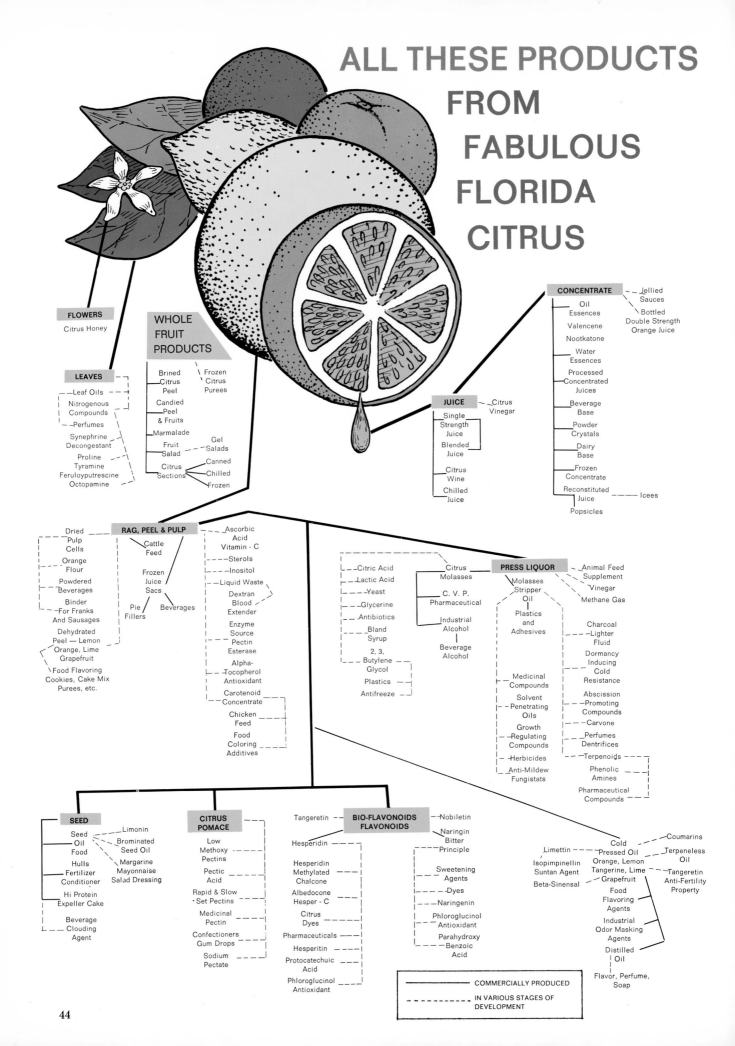

ALL THESE PRODUCTS FROM FABULOUS FLORIDA CITRUS

FLOWERS
Citrus Honey

LEAVES
- Leaf Oils
- Nitrogenous Compounds
- Perfumes
- Synephrine Decongestant
- Proline
- Tyramine
- Feruloyputrescine
- Octopamine

WHOLE FRUIT PRODUCTS
- Brined Citrus Peel
- Candied Peel & Fruits
- Marmalade
- Fruit Salad
- Citrus Sections
- Frozen Citrus Purees
- Gel Salads
- Canned
- Chilled
- Frozen

JUICE
- Single Strength Juice
- Blended Juice
- Citrus Wine
- Chilled Juice
- Citrus Vinegar

CONCENTRATE
- Oil Essences
- Valencene
- Nootkatone
- Water Essences
- Processed Concentrated Juices
- Beverage Base
- Powder Crystals
- Dairy Base
- Frozen Concentrate
- Reconstituted Juice
- Popsicles
- Jellied Sauces
- Bottled Double Strength Orange Juice
- Icees

RAG, PEEL & PULP
- Dried Pulp Cells
- Orange Flour
- Powdered Beverages
- Binder For Franks And Sausages
- Dehydrated Peel — Lemon Orange, Lime Grapefruit
- Food Flavoring Cookies, Cake Mix Purees, etc.
- Cattle Feed
- Frozen Juice Sacs
- Pie Fillers
- Beverages
- Ascorbic Acid Vitamin - C
- Sterols
- Inositol
- Liquid Waste
- Dextran Blood Extender
- Enzyme Source Pectin Esterase
- Alpha-Tocopherol Antioxidant
- Carotenoid Concentrate
- Chicken Feed
- Food Coloring Additives

- Citric Acid
- Lactic Acid
- Yeast
- Glycerine
- Antibiotics
- Bland Syrup
- 2, 3, Butylene Glycol
- Plastics
- Antifreeze

- Citrus Molasses
- C. V. P. Pharmaceutical
- Industrial Alcohol
- Beverage Alcohol

PRESS LIQUOR
- Molasses Stripper Oil
- Plastics and Adhesives
- Medicinal Compounds
- Solvent Penetrating Oils
- Growth Regulating Compounds
- Herbicides
- Anti-Mildew Fungistats
- Animal Feed Supplement
- Vinegar
- Methane Gas
- Charcoal Lighter Fluid
- Dormancy Inducing Cold Resistance
- Abscission Promoting Compounds
- Carvone
- Perfumes Dentrifices
- Terpenoids
- Phenolic Amines
- Pharmaceutical Compounds

SEED
- Seed Oil Food
- Hulls
- Fertilizer Conditioner
- Hi Protein Expeller Cake
- Beverage Clouding Agent
- Limonin
- Brominated Seed Oil
- Margarine Mayonnaise Salad Dressing

CITRUS POMACE
- Low Methoxy Pectins
- Pectic Acid
- Rapid & Slow Set Pectins
- Medicinal Pectin
- Confectioners Gum Drops
- Sodium Pectate

- Tangeretin
BIO-FLAVONOIDS FLAVONOIDS
- Hesperidin
- Hesperidin Methylated Chalcone
- Albedocone Hesper - C
- Citrus Dyes
- Pharmaceuticals
- Hesperitin
- Protocatechuic Acid
- Phloroglucinol Antioxidant
- Nobiletin
- Naringin Bitter Principle
- Sweetening Agents
- Dyes
- Naringenin
- Phloroglucinol Antioxidant
- Parahydroxy Benzoic Acid

- Limettin
- Isopimpinellin Suntan Agent
- Beta-Sinensal
- Cold Pressed Oil Orange, Lemon Tangerine, Lime Grapefruit
- Food Flavoring Agents
- Industrial Odor Masking Agents
- Distilled Oil
- Flavor, Perfume, Soap
- Coumarins
- Terpeneless Oil
- Tangeretin Anti-Fertility Property

———— COMMERCIALLY PRODUCED

‑ ‑ ‑ ‑ IN VARIOUS STAGES OF DEVELOPMENT

44

NECTARINE HARVEST PERIODS

White sections on the chart show normal harvest periods by weeks. Storage of some of the midseason and late varieties makes them available longer than the periods indicated on the chart. The first five varieties listed could, and occasionally do, start shipping the last week of May.

VARIETY (in order of appearance)	1972 PROD. 000 PKGS.
ARM KING	51
MAY GRAND	231
SUNBRIGHT	67
RED JUNE	396
JUNE GRAND	76
EARLY SUN GRAND	1241
INDEPENDENCE	334
SUN GRAND	940
STAR GRAND	113
FLAVOR TOP	50
GRANDERLI	171
FANTASIA	93
RED GRAND	537
LE GRAND	476
CLINTON STRAWBERRY	47
LATE LE GRAND	930
REGAL GRAND	230
GOLD KING	430
FLAME KIST	105
AUTUMN GRAND	318
RICHARD'S GRAND	62
SEPTEMBER GRAND	257
OTHERS	480
TOTAL	7,635

ORANGES

China is placed as the home of this citrus fruit, with Columbus being given credit for introducing seeds to the New World.

Like grapefruit, oranges are an excellent source of Vitamin C, which the body needs to replace daily in order to maintain good standards of health. An average 8-ounce glass of orange juice contains more than enough of this essential Vitamin for daily body requirements.

An even greater percentage of Vitamin C, and other health-giving properties are obtained when the juice *and* pulp are eaten! They're low in sodium, low in calories — are one of the "detergent" fruits recommended by the ADA for dental health — an excellent tooth cleanser!

As in the case of grapefruit . . . or any other member of the citrus family . . . the weight of an orange is indicative of its juice content. Also bear this point in mind: Make sure the fruit is firm and has a skin that is not too rough.

Color is not a sure guide to quality, as much of the Florida and Texas crop has coloring added to the outer skin. Such fruit is dipped in, or sprayed with, a harmless vegetable dye solution at packing time. This process has absolutely *no effect* on the eating quality of the fruit; it simply gives the outer skin the deep orange color expected by consumers. The law requires that all oranges treated this way must be stamped "Color Added" and must have passed very strict maturity tests.

Florida, California and Arizona — in that order — make up this country's principal orange-producing states. Valencias, the most important variety, are shipped from Florida, February through June, and from California mainly from late April through October. California Navels are available mainly November through May (these two major varieties dominate the production of California and Arizona and the shipping season for the two states is approximately the same).

Other less important Western orange varieties are the Jaffa, Malta, Blood (identifiable by the deep red color of its meat). All are usually in season from the middle of March until about the middle of May.

Early Florida varieties include the Hamlin, a smooth-

HOW TO PREPARE FRESH **ORANGES**

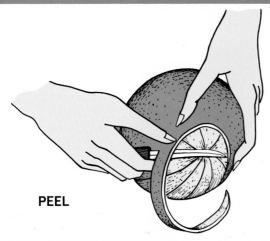

PEEL

TO PEEL ORANGES MOST EASILY: Run a sharp knife between the peel and the meat in spiral fashion, like peeling an apple, using a sawing motion.

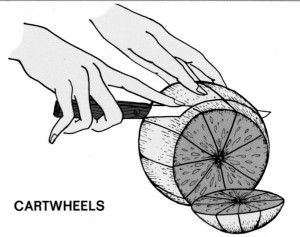

CARTWHEELS

TO MAKE ORANGE CARTWHEELS: Cut peeled or unpeeled oranges into crosswise slices any thickness desired. Use in salads, for broiling, meat accompaniments or as a garnish.

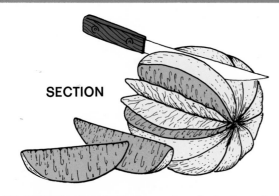

SECTION

TO SECTION ORANGES: Run a sharp knife alongside of a dividing membrane, cutting it to the center of orange. At the core, twist the knife and bring the blade back out, separating the section from the membrane on the other side. With practice, this can be done in one continuous motion and very quickly. Hold the orange over a bowl to save the juice. Use sections in salads, fruit cups, desserts and as a garnish.

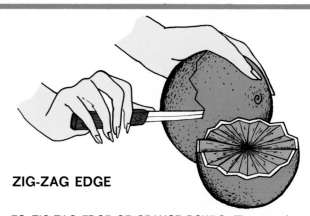

ZIG-ZAG EDGE

TO ZIG-ZAG EDGE OF ORANGE BOWLS: Thrust a sharp pointed knife into center of orange at an angle and pull it out. Make the next cut at opposite angle. Repeat all around orange, turning knife alternately at right angles and left. This forms a zig-zag edge for the two orange halves. Pull 2 halves in opposite directions to divide the orange into halves.

skinned seedless type, followed closely by the seedy Parson Brown and Pineapple.

Texas and Mexico are becoming increasingly important as orange-producing areas, with varieties and seasons somewhat similar to Florida.

Varieties of oranges are generally divided into two general classifications of *sour* and *sweet*. The former is valuable only as a rootstock, but it is grown in some countries, particularly Spain, for its bitter or sour fruits. Mandarins or tangerines are considered distinct from the sweet orange grown in the U. S., but the tangor hybrid Temple orange represents a sizeable volume.

The sweet orange can be divided into four principal kinds: the common, such as the Florida or California valencia; the blood, or pigmented orange, such as the ruby; the acidless orange grown in some Mediterranean areas; and the navel orange, grown principally in California, but to smaller extent in Florida and Texas. But, these are not botanical classifications.

To dispel some common thinking about oranges: many say that California orange groves are being replaced by homes; not so: today there are more trees growing oranges in California than there were ten years ago, with higher production per tree than ever. Despite popular thinking, Florida produces about four times as many oranges as California and Arizona combined; however, a much greater percentage of Florida's production is used for process purposes than the other two States.

In the U. S., fresh oranges are available in some volume every month of the year, peak supply generally December through March.

In California orange production, statistics relate to

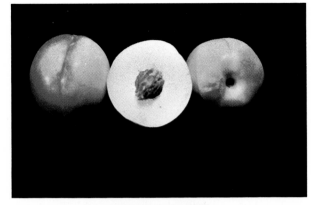

LATE LE GRAND

ROSE NECTARINE

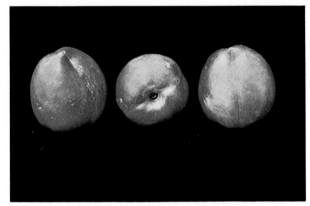

SUN GRAND NECTARINE

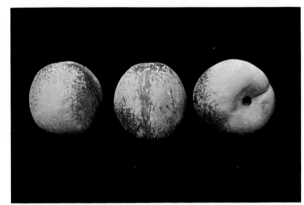

EARLY LE GRAND

NAVEL

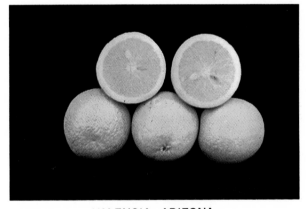

VALENCIA, ARIZONA

VALENCIA, RE-GREEN

VALENCIA

the two principal varieties of navel and valencia. In the latter crop, 37-56% is marketed fresh, domestic; 7-15% is exported and 37-53% in recent years is diverted to process or "other uses". For navels, historically, 69-81% is marketed fresh, domestic, 3-4% is exported and 16-39% generally around 20%, is processed or utilized in some other manner.

California orange production in recent years has been relocated to other areas than those of a few years ago; today, Central and Northern districts grow more than six times the volume of Southern districts of the State.

Valencia oranges, regardless of where produced, have a tendency late in the season to turn from a bright orange hue to a greenish tinge, particularly around the stem end. Do not be misled by this change in color, *as it affects only the outer skin.* Actually these oranges are amply matured and the inside is fully ripe, sweet and juicy.

Optimum storage conditions are 32° F. and 90% relative humidity. A common phrase, "Best for Juice and Every Use" applies to this fruit. For hand-eating, salads, added as a topping to ice cream or day-old cake, oranges will add zest.

Newlyweds used to refer to the orange crates they were using in place of costly furniture. You haven't heard this lately because the industry rarely uses a wooden shipping container. Most oranges are shipped in corrugated cartons with a 4/5ths or 3/5ths bushel content.

Since all oranges are still identified for size by count (72s, 88s being much larger than 113s or 100s), for the reason mentioned above — container size — few even in the industry recognize that a Florida orange of the same count size is approximately one size larger than the same count size from California, Arizona or Texas!

Recent studies on the health merits of the orange seem to indicate we know very little of its merits. In truth, we probably know more about the surface of the moon than we do about the inside of an orange! The major thrust now is toward learning what the components can do in terms of better human health. Studies recently produced data indicating that the Vitamin C in orange juice not only reduced the cholesterol level in blood, but also reduced the triglyceride level and the amount of ascorbone. Since both cholesterol and triglyceride are believed to cause, or at least be associated with, atherosclerosis, these data appear significant for human health.

And there is a persistent and widely-held belief that nutrients in fruits and vegetables are concentrated in and just below the skin. For instance, it is known there is more iron per 100 grams of California navel orange

peel than in the same amount of juice; but, there is more iron in the total edible part of the orange than in the peel; thus, one of the reasons for recommending eating the whole edible portion of fresh oranges, rather than just the juice — much more healthful!

And if you want to be beautiful, according to the Florida Department of Citrus, an orange half is an excellent astringent and will cure a shiny complexion when rubbed on the face!

As a concluding thought about oranges, remember this: whichever kind you purchase, look for the name "Blue Goose" stamped on the skin. It is placed there for your protection to give you the best in value for the money you spend. This nationally-famous trademark identifies "the best of the better crops".

PEACHES

Like so many of our tree fruits today, authorities generally agree that the original home of the peach is China, better than 2000 years ago, and from there the peach was probably transported into Persia, for the botanical name of the peach is from the Latin, meaning, "Persian". For many years, they were apparently called "Persian Apples".

If you have ever cracked a peach stone and tasted the nut inside, you found it decidedly resembled an almond in taste. (Unlike the almond, the peach nut should not be eaten.) This taste resemblance indicates the peach we know today is a prototype of the wild almond, cultivated to near its present taste in ancient Persia.

Peaches are grown commercially in almost all sections of the U. S. — wherever winter temperatures do not fall below −12 or −15°. Total U. S. peach production has been around the 3.2-3.5 billion pounds yearly, with California having 60% of the National production, leading all States. South Carolina, with 10% of the total, and Georgia with 6%, are runners up. The South leads in production of peaches for the fresh market, supplying 50% of the total. California grows nearly all peaches used for processing.

Weeks of peach availability in the U. S. are rather small, the season generally beginning about May 10 in California, ending about October 20 from Washington State.

Peaches are one of the oldest known, and most versatile fruits, maintaining a popularity with consumers that ranks among the best, such as oranges, apples and bananas. Their versatility as a fruit is demonstrated by the fact that they are available in a multitude of forms — fresh, canned, frozen, dried, pickled, spiced and pureed, to name but a few.

BABCOCK

INDIAN, WHITE FLESH

FAY ELBERTA

PETERSON ELBERTA

RED HAVEN

RIO-OSO-GEM

SPRINGTIME

The consumer can buy the fresh and easily use them for salads, baking, preserves, wine, brandies, ice cream, low calorie snacks and a wide variety of other food and beverage preparations. The single most important use of the National peach crop is canning.

When purchasing peaches, the best thing to remember is that they must look good to be good. Buy peaches which are fairly firm, or becoming a trifle soft. A red color, or "blush" on the peach, in varying degrees, is not, alone, a true sign of edible quality. The skin color between the red areas (ground color) should be yellow, or at least creamy. Avoid very firm or hard peaches with a distinctly green ground color, for they are probably immature and will not ripen properly. Don't buy peaches with large, flattened bruises, for they will not ripen properly. Over-ripeness is generally indicated by the deeper reddish-brown color and a softness of the fruit — even a shriveling of the skin at the stem end. Peaches in this stage are suitable for immediate use, but cannot be held for any length of time.

From purely a health standpoint, the peach ranks high in its average content of Vitamin A, and contains some noticeable quantity of Vitamin C. A 3½ oz. edible portion contains 46 calories, 160-259 mg. of potassium and a fair, but representative, portion of all other minerals. Thus, it makes an ideal low calorie fruit for in-between-meal snacks that are beneficial and won't add extra pounds in satisfying hunger.

Eaten raw, it is one of the important detergent fruits helpful to dental health.

New varieties, with more exterior glamour and taste appeal, are fast replacing some old favorites, such as the Elberta. In a general way, all early-maturing varieties, all production areas, are either clingstone or semi-cling, all others are freestone. The hundreds of known peach varieties are classified in this manner, clingstone or freestone. In freestone varieties, the fruit can be easily separated from the stone or pit; in clingstones, as implied by the name, the flesh adheres tightly to the pit. Both types may have either yellow or white flesh.

To some extent, varieties grown in Western States are somewhat different from the varieties grown in Southern and Eastern States. Following is a listing of California varieties in order of appearance on the market: Springtime (white flesh, semi-clingstone), Mayflower (white flesh, clingstone), Robin (white flesh, semi-clingstone), Blazing Gold (yellow flesh, semi-freestone), Cardinal (yellow flesh, clingstone), Royal May (yellow flesh, semi-clingstone), Gold Dust (yellow flesh, semi-clingstone), Merrell Gem (yellow flesh, clingstone), Dixired (yellow flesh, clingstone), Merrell Gemfree (yellow flesh, freestone), Coronet (yellow flesh, freestone), Redhaven (yellow flesh, freestone), Babcock (white flesh, freestone), Redtop, Early Elberta, Redglobe, Merrell 49'er, Elberta, Fay Elberta, J. H. Hale and Rio Oso Gem, the latter eight being yellow freestone.

In the Southern and Eastern States, particularly Southern, peach varieties in order of appearance on the market: Maygold, Redcap (yellow flesh, clingstone), Cardinal, Dixired, Sunhaven (yellow flesh, clingstone), Coronet, Jerseyland (yellow flesh, semi-clingstone), Redhaven, Triogem, Keystone, Suwanee, Washington, Ranger, Sunhigh, Richhaven, Southland, Loring, Redglobe, Monroe, Jefferson, Madison, Sullivan Elberta, Blake, Redskin, Elberta, Dixiland, Jefferson, J. H. Hale, Rio Oso Gem. The latter varieties are all yellow flesh, freestone.

Hydrocooling peaches is a common practice in Eastern and Southern States. It is a process whereby peaches pass .over a continuous chain conveyor and are subjected to a shower of ice water, which may contain a fungicide solution. The pit temperature of the fruit usually is reduced by 20-30° in .15-20 minutes, thereby.

Peaches are hydrocooled after packing, although a few shippers hydrocool fruit prior to packing. The process reduces the temperature of the fruit rapidly and delays ripening and decay during transit. It also permits marketing ripe fruit, reduces shipping and marketing losses, results in better quality peaches for the consumer.

In other areas of production, precooling the fruit, generally after packing, in dry cold storage or refrigerated cars, is an accepted method of preserving quality.

Fairly recent tests — we don't know of any commercial applications at this writing — employs the use of hot water to control shipping point decay in peaches. Submersion of peaches in 120° F. water for 7 minutes, or 130° for 3 minutes, before holding at 70°, effectively reduced both brown rot and Rhizopus rot, the two biggest enemies of the peach.

Today, most peaches are thoroughly brushed before shipping — employing soft, dry brushes, or with a new water-brush system.

Peaches ripen rapidly at room temperature. But if they are to be held, 32° F. and 90% relative humidity is ideal.

Peaches can be peeled easily by dipping them in boiling water for 20-30 seconds and then plunging them immediately into ice water. The skins will slip off readily.

One cup of sliced peaches weighs 168 gr. (6 oz.) One pound of medium size peaches will serve four people.

BARTLETT

SECKEL

BOSC

BUENA HARDY

D'ANJOU

FURELLE

PEAR APPLES, SALAD PEARS

PRICKLY PEAR

PEARS

The pear apparently was used as food by Stone Age men and was later improved by the ancient Greeks. Pears were nicknamed "butter fruit" in the early 1700's, due to the soft, melting flesh.

There are literally thousands of varieties of pears — but only a few are grown for commercial marketing today. (More than 3,000 varieties are known in the U. S., but less than a dozen are commercially important.) Behind the cultivation of such a large number of varieties lies a story about the landed gentry of France about 1850. At that time, it was the style, just as dog or horse raising is today, to see who could produce the finest species of pears. As a result, scores of new types came into being very quickly — and almost all of them were just as quickly forgotten, once the fad was dropped.

From this French "horticultural spree" came many of the fall and winter pears found on the market today. Pears are grown in commercial quantities only in 11 States, with California growing more than one-half the total, and Oregon-California-Washington growing about 90% of the total production.

Pears are packed and shipped green, because it is characteristic that they develop a finer flavor and smoother texture when ripened off the tree — the sugar content increases, due to conversion of starch to sugar. Maturity before picking is determined in a variety of ways, but mainly through determining soluble solids with a refractometer (see "Apples"). Firmness of fruit, also a maturity guide, is determined with a pressure tester, an instrument using a 5/16″ diameter plunger applied to a peeled portion of the fruit; the pressure required to penetrate the fruit may run from 10 to 23 pounds, depending on district of production and variety.

BARTLETT. Principal variety grown in the three Western States, also the important commercial pear in Michigan and New York. Known as the summer pear, is bell-shaped, skin fairly thin, clear-yellow in color when ripe. Occasionally blushed, surface somewhat uneven. Flesh white, smooth and juicy. On the market from July through November, Bartletts are famous for both their dessert quality and for canning.

D'ANJOU. On the market from October through May, this variety is medium to large in size with short neck, flesh yellowish-white, fairly fine, buttery, juicy, some grit cells at center; spicy, sweet flavor. Stores well. Color is not an indication of ripeness on the Anjou — it may be yellow, yellowish-green or green. If it yields to gentle pressure of your thumb at the stem end, it is

in the "breaking" process and is ready for sale. The oval-shaped Anjou is the principal variety of winter pear.

BOSC. Skin color is dark yellow overlaid with a cinnamon-russet, which may vary in intensity. Fruit is medium or large in size, with flesh yellowish-white, some grit at the center, buttery, very juicy. Long, tapering neck. Called the "aristocrat of pears". Excellent for fresh eating and baking.

COMICE. Fruit is medium to large, sometimes very large and almost round in shape; skin fairly thick, granular, sometimes russeted, greenish-yellow in color; flesh very fine, melting, extremely juicy, no grit. Regarded by many as the standard of dessert quality among pears. Famous as a holiday gift pear.

Pears are one of the most delicious and tempting fruits of all and are on the market in some volume all year around. In making your selections, don't be misled by a scar or minor surface blemish, as this in no way affects the fruit's inner delicacy. As a matter of fact, many of the most delectable pears have a highly russeted skin.

All of the winter pears are rich in levulose sugar — a valuable aid to diabetics, as their system can better tolerate this than glucose. Pears have a fair content of Vitamin C, some Vitamin A and most other healthful, body-building minerals vital to good nutrition. It has been found that pear juice contained all the B vitamins. In 100 grams (3½ oz.) of edible portion, this fruit provides 61 calories.

The Seckel is a late summer pear, small, sweet and luscious, richly russeted and excellent for eating out of hand. Another russet pear, very sweet in flavor, is the Winter Nelis, medium to small size with excellent cooking qualities. The Red Bartlett differs from the regular Bartlett in that the color is bright crimson — the size, shape and qualities are the same. Another winter pear is the Forelle, which is very attractive, highly colored with bright red blush and red freckles, golden yellow. Later winter variety is the Packham, a medium to large pear with a bumpy surface, also the leading variety imported in spring. This variety is green and turns to yellow as it ripens. The Eldorado is an average-sized winter variety which resembles the Bartlett. Best eaten from January through March.

Pears should be fully ripe for "fresh" use, such as eating out of hand, salads or shortcakes. If they are hard and unyielding to the touch at time of purchasing, allow them to stand at ordinary room temperatures until the flesh responds readily to a gentle pressure of the hand, just as does a ripe peach. They are then — and only then — in prime condition for eating. However,

RED BARTLETT

HAWAIIAN PINEAPPLE

for baking and cooking purposes, pears are best when they are still firm and slightly under-ripe.

PINEAPPLES

The pineapple is a tropical fruit, so named because of its resemblance to the pine cone in shape and appearance. It is universally popular for desserts, salads and for canning, since it not only possesses an exquisite flavor, but has good Vitamin C (ascorbic acid) and high natural sugar content as well. It is low in sodium content, has an alkaline reaction in the body and provides only 52 calories per 3½ oz. edible portion, raw. It also contains fairly reputable quantities of minerals and 70 I.U. of Vitamin A.

There are very few pineapples shipped for fresh sales that are ripened on the plant. While the general advice to a consumer is to "ripen before cutting", our best advice is to select fruit that is mature, for the physiology of a pineapple is such that it *cannot ripen after harvest*, since it does not have a starch reserve. Thus, unlike the banana and pear, there is no material to convert to sugar. What actually happens, in holding a pineapple after harvest, is that the shell color changes somewhat, the fruit becomes soft, and, through respiration, it loses some of its acid present at harvest. Through this loss, one might say it *"ripens"*, but it is only a depletion of part of the original composition.

In choosing a pineapple, select one that is plump and fresh looking and as large as possible; the larger the fruit, the greater the proportion of edible flesh. Fresh, deep-green crown leaves are a good sign, but contrary to popular belief, the ease with which these leaves can be pulled out is not necessarily a sure sign of quality. Thumping is of no value. Avoid fruit that is old looking, dry, with brown leaves. Fragrance is a good sign. Avoid bruised fruit, or those with soft spots. A very slight separation of the eyes (pips) generally

indicate maturity. Over-maturity is most frequently shown by slight decay at the base or on the sides with dark, soft, watery spots.

To lose some of the natural acid present in pineapples, keep at room temperature, away from heat or sun — then refrigerate at 45° F., relative humidity of 85-90%. Pineapples are very sensitive to chilling, when not fully ripe.

Hawaii, Puerto Rico and Mexico supply most of the fresh pineapples used in the U. S., the shipping season being at its height between April and June.

The pineapple plant is grown from slips, crown or suckers — not seeds — with the leading variety in the world being the Smooth Cayenne. Generally, each plant produces only one pine and takes about 20 months to grow and mature.

For those of you who like unusual decorations in the home, try this: cut off the top of a pineapple and plant it in a small jar of water. It will soon send out rootlets and grow into a very attractive palm.

Fresh pineapples are sliced, grated or cubed and eaten plain, dipped in sugar, or mixed with other fruits. They are used as an appetizer, salad or dessert. Add to lemon pies, cook with meats or combine with cheese chunks for hors d'oeuvres.

53

PLUMS

Although plums came to America from Europe, they are believed to have originated in Western Asia in the region south of the Caucasus Mountains. The species dates back at least 2,000 years. The early colonists in America found native plums from New England to Florida. They were eaten by the Indians long before the colonial period. More than 75% of the world supply of prunes and plums is grown in California!

Plums come in a bewildering variety. There are more than 2,000 varieties but it is fairly easy to become an expert if you remember there are two main types — the *Japanese* varieties and the *European* varieties.

The Japanese varieties are medium to large — they are famous for their juiciness. They may be a variety of shapes, but *never* blue or purple.

European varieties are *always* blue or purple. They are generally smaller, oval or roundish. Compared to Japanese varieties, most European plums are milder in flavor and have a firmer texture.

Following are some of the more popular plum varieties, in approximate order of appearance on the market:

RED BEAUT. Firm, yellow-colored flesh, bright red exterior. One of the earliest varieties.

BEAUTY. Medium-sized, heart-shaped, bright crimson in color when ripe. Flesh is amber, streaked with scarlet.

BURMOSA. Semi-heart-shaped, attractive in appearance with a red blush. Flesh is light amber, soft and fine-textured with flavor mild and pleasant.

SANTA ROSA. Perhaps the "Queen" of plums, there is the regular Santa Rosa and the late Santa Rosa, referring particularly to maturity. Conical in shape, purplish-crimson in color, the flesh is yellow to dark red near the skin. A rich, pleasing-tart flavor and very juicy.

WICKSON. Large, heart-shaped, yellow skin with whitish bloom and ripens to a yellow-red color. Flesh is bright yellow, juicy, excellent flavor.

TRAGEDY. Medium in size, oval in shape, skin is dark blue-purple in color with a yellow-green, firm flesh. Sweet and well-flavored.

MARIPOSA. A red-fleshed plum, almost perfectly round in shape, skin color is red with a very heavy cover of gray bloom, and, as the fruit ripens, it becomes dark, red-purple in color.

EL DORADO. Black-red skin with light amber flesh that turns to pink when cooked. Firm, easy to slice and holds shape well when canned or cooked.

LARODA. Generally a large plum with medium red over-color, yellow under-color. Yellow flesh, good "shipper".

DUARTE. Dark red or dull-red skin, flesh is dark red when ripe; juicy and good flavor. Heart-shaped.

NUBIANA. Large, flat type with oval shape; purple-black at maturity; yellow flesh, hard, good flavor.

QUEEN ANN. Large plum with deep, mahogany color. Flesh is light amber in color throughout, and when fully mature, has a rich, honey-like flavor.

PRESIDENT. Fruit is large, oval-shaped, very dark purple in color, good texture and flavor, outer skin generally has a "frosty" look.

SIM-KA (also called *NEW YORKER*). A large plum, has purple-colored skin and yellow flesh with good keeping quality.

RED ROSA. Purplish-red colored skin, yellow flesh. Good keeping quality.

CASSELMAN. A bud mutation of Late Santa Rosa, similar in size and shape, but has a lighter red over-color and ripens a few days later.

ELEPHANT HEART. A large fruit with bright red flesh, excellent dessert quality.

SHARKEY. Round, mottled red on yellow background; yellow flesh, good flavor.

SUGAR. Oval shape, purple skin; yellow, dry, sweet meat.

STANDARD. Dark blue in color with yellow flesh.

Prunes are actually a variety of plum particularly suitable for drying purposes, as a fresh, ripe prune can be separated from the pit like a freestone peach. They are blue-black, oval, firm-fleshed and represent the late plum crop. The Italian variety is most commonly shipped in the fresh stage, with most supplies coming from Oregon, Idaho and Washington. Italian prune-plums are rich in iron and a good source of Vitamins A and B. They are ideal for home canning or freezing, and are extremely high in fruit sugar — a natural energy food and easily digested.

If you want plenty of Vitamin A, try eating a few fresh prunes or plums. They have a high concentration of this element, plus a fair quantity of the all-important Vitamin C. They are low in calories and sodium. Some fresh prunes have a high mineral content, too, particularly those coming from Eastern Oregon and Southwestern Idaho. The volcanic ash soil prevalent in that region transmits these healthful qualities to the products grown there.

Quality characteristics for both plums and prunes are similar. They should be good color for the variety, in fairly firm-to-slightly-soft stage of ripeness—soft enough to yield to slight pressure.

Plums and fresh prunes are excellent eaten out of

hand. They have a refreshing tart sweetness. They make good pies, stewed fruit, preserves, jellies and jams and are tasty in ice cream, puddings and Bavarian creams; in cakes, tarts and pastries.

Optimum storage conditions are 32° F. and 90% relative humidity.

For many years, the principal shipping container for plums has been the four-basket wood crate, holding 27-31 lbs. of fruit, and necessitating considerable labor to place-pack the baskets. (For prune plums, principal container has been a 28 lb. ring-faced basket.)

The industry has started to switch to a "tight-fill" pack, which will probably increase in future volume. Instead of requiring considerable hand labor, fruit is directly conveyed from the grading belt to the container, giving a special three-second machine vibration to allow the fruit to "nest" properly, weighed to 30 lbs. net, a tightly-fitting lid placed on the container to prevent vertical motion of the fruit during shipping. Generally, fibreboard containers are used for this method.

Per capita fresh plum-prune consumption is 1-2 lbs. annually.

SANTA ROSA

SATSUMA

STANDARD

WICKSON

ITALIAN PRUNES

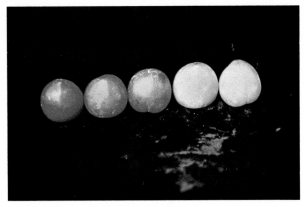

BEAUTY

DUARTE

EL DORADO

ELEPHANT HEART

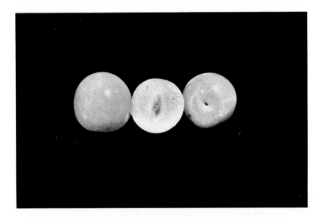

GREEN GAGE

LARODA

NUBIANA

QUEEN ANN

GUIDE TO:

AVERAGE MONTHLY AVAILABILITY OF
FRESH FRUITS & VEGETABLES

The following chart shows the availability of 66 different fresh fruits and vegetables or groups, with information on major commodities by main states, making a total of 128 lines of entries. Availability is expressed as a monthly percentage of total annual supply, which is in the righthand column. The figures are based on five years of statistics of the U.S. Department of Agriculture or Department of Commerce. All percentages are rounded, so do not necessarily total 100.

MONTHLY AVAILABILITY EXPRESSED AS PERCENTAGE OF TOTAL ANNUAL SUPPLY

COMMODITY	Jan. %	Feb. %	Mar. %	Apr. %	May %	June %	July %	Aug. %	Sept. %	Oct. %	Nov. %	Dec. %	ANNUAL TOTAL million lbs.
APPLES, ALL	10	10	10	8	7	4	2	3	10	13	11	11	3,284
„ WASHINGTON	10	11	13	11	11	7	3	1	5	8	9	12	1,435
„ NEW YORK	10	10	12	10	8	4	1	2	9	13	10	10	414
„ MICHIGAN	12	11	11	8	4	1	*	2	8	17	13	13	269
APRICOTS					2	55	37	5					40
ARTICHOKES	6	8	13	21	15	5	3	3	4	6	9	6	59
ASPARAGUS, ALL		2	20	34	27	16	1			*	*		109
„ CALIFORNIA		3	31	48	12	5	1			*	*		78
„ NEW JERSEY				7	58	34	1						27
AVOCADOS, ALL	10	9	10	9	9	8	7	7	7	7	8	9	119
„ CALIFORNIA	10	10	12	11	11	9	8	7	6	5	5	7	101
„ FLORIDA	12	3	*	*			3	7	10	18	27	21	17
BANANAS	8	8	9	9	9	9	8	7	8	9	8	9	3,650
BEANS, ALL	6	5	6	8	10	13	12	11	9	9	7	6	396
„ FLORIDA	13	12	15	20	13	2	*			2	11	14	149
BEETS	4	4	5	5	7	13	15	13	12	11	7	4	99
BERRIES, MISC. (A)					3	26	49	12	4	4	2		5
BLUEBERRIES					3	29	38	26	4				43
BROCCOLI	10	10	12	11	9	5	4	4	6	10	11	9	59

MONTHLY AVAILABILITY EXPRESSED AS PERCENTAGE OF TOTAL ANNUAL SUPPLY												
COMMODITY	Jan. %	Feb. %	Mar. %	Apr. %	May %	June %	July %	Aug. %	Sept. %	Oct. %	Nov. %	Dec. %	ANNUAL TOTAL million lbs.
BRUSSELS SPR.	14	11	7	3	2	1	*	2	10	17	19	15	20
CABBAGE, ALL	9	8	10	9	9	9	8	7	8	8	8	8	1,860
,, FLORIDA	18	16	22	24	11	1					1	8	326
,, TEXAS	17	15	19	13	5	2	1	2	1	2	8	15	273
,, CALIFORNIA	10	12	13	11	12	9	6	5	5	6	6	7	259
,, NEW YORK	13	9	6	2		1	6	8	11	13	15	15	175
,, NEW JERSEY	*					19	25	17	14	14	9	2	126
CANTALOUPES, ALL			1	4	9	21	22	25	11	4	1		1,563
,, CALIFORNIA					1	10	25	39	18	6	2	*	844
,, MEXICO	*	1	8	28	43	20	1					*	240
,, ARIZONA					1	56	41	*		1	1		203
,, TEXAS					21	49	14	12	4	*			148
CARROTS, ALL	10	9	10	9	8	8	8	7	8	8	8	8	1,365
,, CALIFORNIA	8	7	8	8	9	11	12	9	7	7	6	7	710
,, TEXAS	13	11	14	13	10	6	5	5	4	4	7	9	472
CAULIFLOWER, ALL	8	7	8	7	5	5	4	5	11	19	14	8	198
,, CALIFORNIA	12	10	13	12	10	7	5	4	4	6	9	9	108
,, NEW YORK						*	3	6	19	39	28	5	46
CELERY, ALL	8	8	9	9	8	8	8	7	7	8	10	10	1,326
,, CALIFORNIA	8	7	8	7	6	9	10	6	6	8	14	11	782
,, FLORIDA	14	14	16	16	16	9	1				3	10	365
CHERRIES					6	44	43	7					79
CHINESE CABBAGE	9	8	8	7	6	8	8	8	9	10	10	9	36
COCONUTS	7	8	9	5	4	4	4	5	9	13	16	17	27
CORN, SWEET, ALL	2	2	3	6	16	17	17	18	11	4	3	3	1,504
,, FLORIDA	4	3	6	12	31	26	4			2	5	5	496
,, CALIFORNIA					8	20	25	18	11	10	7	1	196
CRANBERRIES, ALL	*								8	19	52	21	40
,, MASSACHUSETTS	1								12	16	41	30	19
,, WISCONSIN									2	22	70	6	8
CUCUMBERS	5	4	5	8	12	13	13	10	8	8	8	6	613
EGGPLANT	8	6	7	7	7	8	8	12	12	9	8	8	79
ENDIVE, BELGIAN	9	16	15	14	11	1			4	9	9	12	3
ESCAROLE-ENDIVE	8	7	9	8	7	9	9	9	9	10	8	7	158
GARLIC	5	8	8	9	6	7	11	11	13	9	8	6	59
GRAPEFRUIT, ALL	12	11	13	11	9	5	3	2	3	10	11	11	1,500
,, FLORIDA	12	12	14	12	8	3	1	*	2	12	12	11	1,140
,, WESTERN	10	10	10	9	12	12	9	9	4	1	5	9	360

MONTHLY AVAILABILITY EXPRESSED AS PERCENTAGE OF TOTAL ANNUAL SUPPLY												
COMMODITY	Jan. %	Feb. %	Mar. %	Apr. %	May %	June %	July %	Aug. %	Sept. %	Oct. %	Nov. %	Dec. %	ANNUAL TOTAL million lbs.
GRAPES	5	3	4	3	2	4	11	17	19	15	11	7	733
GREENS	10	9	11	10	8	7	6	6	7	8	8	9	289
HONEYDEWS	*	6	12	7	4	12	10	19	20	10	2	*	244
LEMONS	7	6	8	8	10	12	12	10	8	7	6	7	495
LETTUCE, ALL	8	7	9	9	9	9	9	9	8	8	8	8	4,214
,, CALIFORNIA	9	9	10	6	9	10	10	10	10	9	5	5	2,596
,, ARIZONA	9	6	10	23	12	3				3	17	18	830
,, NEW YORK					*	15	41	24	14	4	1		114
,, NEW JERSEY					7	34	10	5	8	22	12	*	110
LIMES	5	4	5	5	8	16	16	13	8	7	6	9	28
MANGOES			4	9	17	31	24	12	2				10
MUSHROOMS	10	9	10	10	8	7	6	5	6	8	10	11	48
NECTARINES	1	4	*			11	33	38	13	*			129
OKRA	*	*	1	4	10	18	23	21	13	7	3	1	38
ONIONS, DRY, ALL	8	7	8	9	9	10	9	9	9	8	8	7	2,300
,, TEXAS	*	*	6	30	31	13	11	7	2	1	*	*	478
,, NEW YORK	10	9	10	6	2	1	1	11	14	13	11	10	392
,, CALIFORNIA	2	1	1	1	11	22	21	16	9	7	5	3	310
ONIONS, GREEN	6	6	8	9	10	11	11	10	8	7	7	7	188
ORANGES, ALL	12	12	13	11	10	6	4	4	4	5	8	12	2,909
,, WESTERN	10	11	13	11	10	8	5	6	6	6	5	10	1,862
,, FLORIDA	15	14	13	11	9	5	1	*		5	12	15	1,004
PAPAYAS, HAWAII	8	8	7	9	11	10	9	7	7	9	9	7	7
PARSLEY & HERBS (B)	7	6	9	8	7	8	7	8	8	10	13	11	80
PARSNIPS	13	11	11	9	7	5	3	3	7	13	11	9	32
PEACHES, ALL					3	24	33	27	12	1			1,326
,, CALIFORNIA					4	23	34	28	8	2			351
,, SOUTH CAROLINA					2	23	51	21	2				257
,, GEORGIA					6	56	35	3					219
PEARS, ALL	7	6	7	6	5	2	5	13	17	15	11	7	426
,, OREGON	14	12	11	7	4	1		*	6	15	17	13	154
,, CALIFORNIA	1	1	1	1	*	*	16	33	26	16	4	2	119
,, WASHINGTON	7	7	8	6	7	3	*	11	18	14	12	8	100
PEAS, GREEN	7	9	11	14	12	14	12	9	5	3	2	3	20
PEPPERS, ALL	7	6	7	7	9	10	10	10	10	9	8	7	533
,, FLORIDA	13	12	16	16	20	13	*				2	8	204
PERSIMMONS	6	1							1	27	42	23	6
PINEAPPLES, ALL	6	8	13	14	14	10	6	5	4	5	7	6	137

MONTHLY AVAILABILITY EXPRESSED AS PERCENTAGE OF TOTAL ANNUAL SUPPLY												
COMMODITY	Jan. %	Feb. %	Mar. %	Apr. %	May %	June %	July %	Aug. %	Sept. %	Oct. %	Nov. %	Dec. %	ANNUAL TOTAL million lbs.
,, PUERTO RICO	5	8	14	14	15	9	6	5	4	6	8	6	73
,, HAWAII	7	8	13	10	11	10	9	8	5	5	7	7	47
PLANTAINS	6	7	8	9	8	9	8	9	9	7	10	10	30
PLUMS-PRUNES	1	1	1		*	16	30	31	19	2			295
POMEGRANATES									5	60	33	2	6
POTATOES, ALL	9	7	9	9	9	9	8	8	8	8	8	8	13,870
,, CALIFORNIA	4	4	4	4	9	25	25	11	5	3	3	4	2,593
,, MAINE	12	11	17	19	17	9	1			8	5	8	1,970
,, IDAHO	13	12	14	15	11	3	*	1	2	7	11	11	1,442
PUMPKINS	1	1	2	2	3	1	1	1	4	79	3	2	46
RADISHES	6	6	8	9	11	12	11	9	8	7	7	7	294
RHUBARB	6	12	16	20	27	14	3	1	*	*	*	*	24
SPINACH	10	9	10	10	10	9	6	5	7	9	9	8	105
SQUASH	7	6	6	7	8	9	9	9	10	11	11	8	327
STRAWBERRIES	2	3	7	16	27	24	9	4	3	2	1	1	287
,, CALIFORNIA	*		3	15	30	22	13	8	5	3	1		166
,, FLORIDA	10	19	44	24	2							2	29
,, MEXICO	16	17	20	9	2					*	11	26	12
SWEETPOTATOES, ALL	9	8	9	7	5	2	3	6	10	12	17	13	989
,, LOUISIANA	8	8	9	7	4	1	4	8	11	12	15	12	279
,, NEW JERSEY	11	11	13	13	9	6	2	1	3	6	14	13	147
,, CALIFORNIA	9	8	9	7	4	4	2	3	8	10	20	16	128
,, N. CAROLINA	11	10	11	9	7	4	1	1	6	8	17	15	116
TANGELOS	13	2								8	40	37	155
TANGERINES	21	6	3	1	*					1	22	45	244
TOMATOES, ALL	6	6	8	8	11	12	11	10	8	8	6	6	2,434
,, FLORIDA	12	11	13	15	23	9	*				5	13	733
,, CALIFORNIA	1	*	*	*	2	7	16	17	15	23	14	4	703
,, MEXICO	13	18	23	21	14	4	1				1	5	375
,, OHIO	1		1	6	17	22	17	8	4	7	11	6	136
TURNIPS-RUTABAGAS	12	11	10	6	5	4	4	5	9	12	13	11	224
,, CANADA	13	11	10	5	2	*	*	4	11	15	18	13	77
WATERMELONS		*	*	2	14	29	30	19	5	*			3,027

NOTES * Indicates supply is less than 0.5% of annual total. (A) Mostly blackberries, dewberries, raspberries. (B) Includes also parsley-root, anise, basil, chives, dill, horseradish and others.

VEGETABLES

ANISE

This plant is a native of temperate Europe and Asia and found mentioned in early recipes around the 11th Century. Was also mentioned in ancient records of Spanish agriculture about 961 A.D.

Anise, also called sweet fennel or finocchi, is similar in appearance to celery, but has a spicy, licorice flavor. This edible type of anise should not be confused with the variety that is grown only for the oil that is secreted by its leaves.

The stocks should be fresh, clean, crisp, solid and of characteristic color. It should be tender and have a well-developed bulb. When the bulb shows extensive brown areas, when the tops are yellow and brown, these are signs of old age or damage from rough handling.

Anise has many applications as a spice, accenting a variety of foods. The bulbs are quartered and eaten raw with salt, or they make an interesting addition to a salad. They may be braised or steamed in any of the ways appropriate for celery — or boiled and served with a cream sauce.

It should be kept refrigerated at 32° F., 95% relative humidity.

Nutritionally, 3½ oz. of anise contains 90% water, 28 calories, high in calcium, phosphorus, iron and very heavy in Vitamin A. Eaten raw, it is one of the important detergent vegetables, helpful to dental health!

ARTICHOKES

Artichokes are one of the oldest foods known to man. It was cultivated as a food in the Mediterranean thousands of years ago, the first recorded development of them for their edible floral heads was in the middle of the 15th Century at Naples, Italy. Early plantings were made in the U. S. by French settlers in Louisiana and the Spanish in the mid-coastal areas of California.

Commercial plantings of artichokes were first made around the beginning of the 20th Century in the mid-coastal areas of California, where the climate is cool, foggy and relatively free of frost. Today, there are over 10,000 acres under cultivation within northern California counties. Castroville, south of San Francisco, is known as the "Artichoke Center of the World".

The Globe artichoke is the large, unopened flower

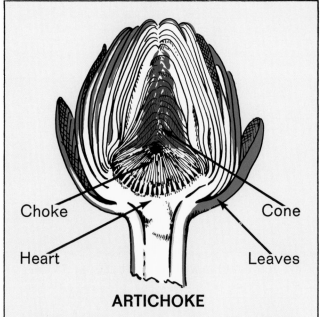

ARTICHOKE

From the leaves, eat the fleshy ends attached to the plant. Lift out the cone and cut out the core (choke), which is the "fuzzy" portion at the center. The heart is a true delicacy that will break readily with fork.

bud of the thistle-like plant which is available all year around — heavy supplies in April and May. Most of the production is from California.

Size has little to do with quality or flavor, but those with compact, heavy, plump globes which yield slightly to pressure and which have large, tightly clinging, fleshy leaf scales of a good, green color are the best. Browning may mean old age, bruise injury or frost.

Winter is the most critical period for artichoke growers. At freezing temperatures, the outer skin of the scales is broken, causing the bud to appear blistered and whitish. After several days, this blistered skin becomes dark and the industry calls them "Winter Kist". Under these conditions, quality is not impaired, but the black appearance has a detrimental effect on sales.

Fresh artichokes add a gourmet feeling to any menu. Cook in salted water with a squeeze of lemon juice to help retain color. A Hollandaise sauce is appropriate with hot artichokes and a vinaigrette sauce when they are served cold. For stuffed artichokes, spread the leaves open, cut off some of the hard tips and remove some of the center leaves; fill with seafood or meat mixture and bake.

They should not be stored for any long period of time but for brief holding, 32° F., and a high humidity of 95% is desirable to prevent wilting or drying.

Nutritionally, 100 grams (3½ ozs.) of edible portion includes 8-44 calories, a rather heavy content of calcium, phosphorus, sodium and potassium, among other elements and minerals.

JERUSALEM artichokes are actually a tuber, the root of a variety of sunflower plant. They are sometimes marketed under the name "sunchokes". One of the true natives of North America, Jerusalem artichokes really aren't artichokes at all and have nothing to do with Jerusalem.

Cooked, they taste slightly like the Globe artichoke; raw, they exhibit crisp, crunchy texture and a delicate nutty flavor. The raw artichokes may be sliced and used in salads, as a garnish to soups or as dunkers for a favorite dip. Broiled, sauteed or mashed, they can serve as a substitute for potatoes. Try them also as an extender for meat loaf, combine them with other vegetables or bake them around a roast.

Food values range from 7 calories per 100 grams for freshly harvested Jerusalem artichokes to 75 calories for those stored for a long period.

ASPARAGUS

Asparagus is a member of the lily family, which also includes such plants as onions, garlic, leeks, lilies, tulips and gladioli. There are only a few varieties of asparagus, and these varieties are of two general types, based on the color of the spears: white and green. The more important group (green) has spears which become dark green in sunlight. The less important group produces light-green, or whitish, spears. These light-colored varieties should not be confused, however, with the white (blanched) asparagus grown for canning.

The green type is an early Spring crop and is usually cut just as soon as the tips of the stalks come above ground about eight inches. The white asparagus is the same variety, but it is clipped while most of the stalk is still below ground.

When selecting your green asparagus at the retail store, look for stalks that are straight and fresh appearing. You will find these crisp and tender with compact, pointed tips and only an inch or so of tough, woody base to trim off at the bottom. On the other hand, asparagus with wilted stalks or loose tips is generally an uneconomical buy, as it is practically certain to be tough and stringy.

At shipping point, asparagus is quickly cooled through a hydrocooling method (see "peaches" for full description). California, New Jersey, Washington and Michigan are chief sources of supply from mid-February to July, peaking from April to June.

If the sweet flavor of the asparagus spear is to be maintained, it must be kept at a temperature below 41° F. and the butt should be kept damp. When it warms up to room temperature, flavor deteriorates rapidly! Suggest storing the asparagus in the coldest part of your refrigerator, wrapped at the base with a damp paper towel kept wet.

Boil asparagus until tender — and no longer! Appropriate sauces are drawn butter and Hollandaise types (hot) and Vinaigrette or mayonnaise (cold). Or, sprinkle lightly with Parmesan cheese and grill. Pieces of cut, fresh asparagus also make a welcome addition to salads.

Asparagus is one of the most perishable commodities shipped commercially in the industry. While conventional truck-rail shipments from Western States have been satisfactory, there has been a large increase in the use of jet air shipments in recent years to assure the consumer of freshness.

A cup of cooked asparagus provides two-thirds of the daily recommended allowance of Vitamin C, a third of the Vitamin A, and about 1/10th of the iron for an adult. It is very low in sodium and calories, generally provides an alkaline reaction in the body.

BEANS

String or stringless beans (practically all produced today are stringless) with long straight pods, crisp enough to snap easily between your fingers, are your best buy. When the beans start to ridge and bulge the pods, they usually are old, tough and leathery. Some string beans are green — others waxy yellow (wax beans). Some are flat and some are round, but all are equally good. Selection depends on personal taste. String beans are found on the market all year and are in reality the immature pods of kidney beans, picked while the seeds are tiny.

Beans are of two general types: *"Bush"* (such as described above) or *"vining"*, such as "pole" beans, the latter growing on trellis or vines, the principal variety of which is the Kentucky Wonder.

Lima beans are flat and kidney-shaped, the smaller sizes being known as *butter limas* and the larger beans as *potato limas*. When making your purchase, look for clean, well-filled pods of a dark green color, as flabby pods generally indicate poor quality. The bean itself should be plump, with a tender skin of good green or greenish-white color.

Fava beans are a comparative newcomer to America. They are a long, round, velvety-podded variety held in high esteem by epicures. They resemble the lima bean except they are rounder, with thick, somewhat larger pods.

Garbanzo beans are the "slick chick" of the pea family. Sometimes called chick peas, they are widely used

ANISE

GREEN ASPARAGUS

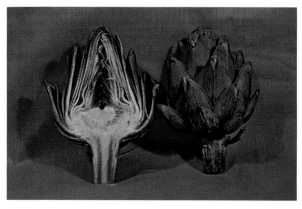

STANDARD ARTICHOKE

JERUSALEM ARTICHOKE

in the Mediterranean and Spanish-American cuisines.

A high Vitamin A content . . . one-third the daily requirement in one-half cup, pressure cooked . . . is the major nutritional value of regular green beans.

Beans can be held successfully for a short period of time at 45-50° F. with relative humidity of 85%. An effective method of storage is to place them in a plastic film bag, which helps greatly to retain moisture, storing them in the hydrator. Washing them before they are placed in the refrigerator will aid in preventing dehydration.

Fresh green or wax snap beans make a generally good nutritional contribution to the diet, although they are not outstanding in any particular nutrient. They are also low in calories.

There are many sauces which will go well with boiled snap beans (Amandine, being one of the most popular), but serving properly cooked, fresh snap beans, au naturel, is a vegetable of tremendous appeal. Fresh beans, cooked tender, tossed with diced potatoes, minced onion and bacon crumbles, make an excellent hot bean salad. They are on the market all year round.

Hot Garbanzos, as a side dish, are good eaten plain with oil or butter. An excellent high-protein food.

When preparing for cooking, they are soaked overnight, or, the beans may be boiled for two minutes in about three times as much water as beans. Season to taste with tomatoes, ketchup or vinegar — add to salads.

Garbanzo beans and lima beans are relatively high in calories.

BEETS

Beets are produced commercially in 31 states with California, New Jersey, Ohio and Texas the main producers. Beets are marketed with or without tops — the fall crop, which is sometimes stored, being the one usually sold with only the root part remaining. They are available the year round.

Fresh, prime quality beets should have a good globular shape, with a smooth, firm flesh and a rich, deep-red color. Those of medium size are less likely to be tough. In the early crop, a poor appearance of the leaves is no certain indication of inferiority, for beet tops deteriorate rapidly without affecting the root quality.

Beet tops are frequently taken from young plants, bunched and sold as salad greens. Here the color and appearance of the tops are important, as their edibility

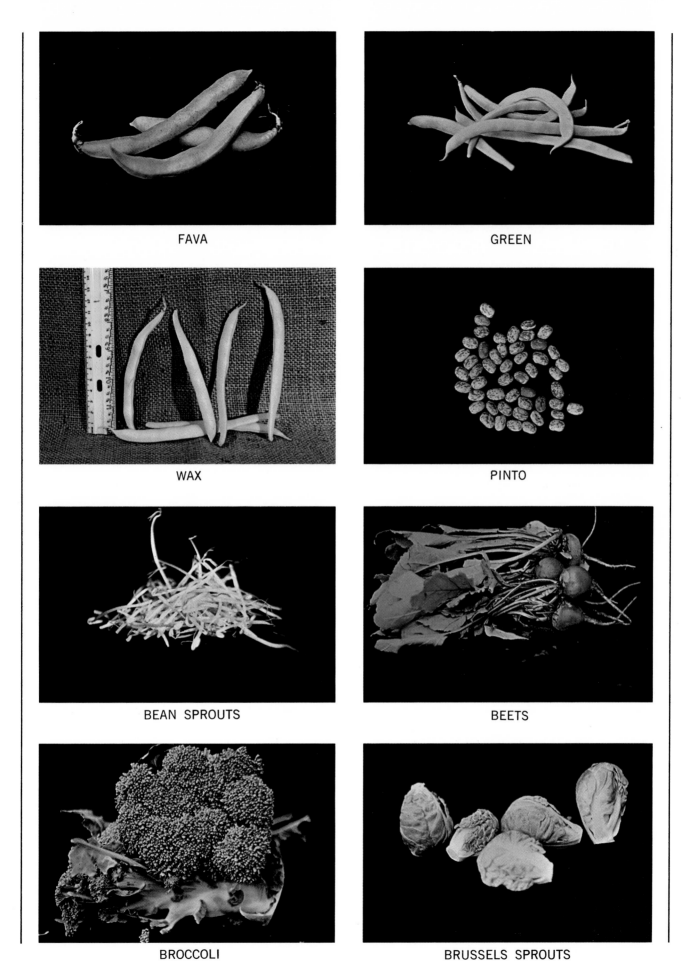

FAVA

GREEN

WAX

PINTO

BEAN SPROUTS

BEETS

BROCCOLI

BRUSSELS SPROUTS

depends upon their being young and tender. Select those that are thin-ribbed, fresh green and not wilted or slimy.

Raw beets on the average are a good source of Vitamin C and a fair source of Vitamin A . . . some of which, however, is lost during cooking. Beet tops, on the other hand, are an amazingly prolific source of Vitamin A. Tests have shown that, when pressure cooked, one-half cup yields over double the daily adult requirements of this food element. Served fresh in a salad, beet greens yield, in addition to their Vitamin A, good quantities of Vitamins C and G. Remember beet greens if you're looking for a low-calorie, vitamin-rich item for your menus.

Best temperature in storage is 32° F., at 95% relative humidity. Bunched beets should be stored only briefly, for the beet tops are extremely perishable.

In preparing beets, don't cut the stem or the root too close, or they will "bleed" in cooking. Cook them in the skins and the skins will slip off readily in your final preparation. Leave them in the cooking liquid until ready to use. Harvard beets remain one of the most popular styles for hot service of beets — and the sweet and sour style (or pickled) for cold service.

BROCCOLI

A member of the cabbage family, Italian broccoli was cultivated as far back as the 16th Century, is a first cousin to cauliflower and served in practically the same way.

When you buy broccoli, look for plenty of green color in the heads as well as the leaves and stems. Size of heads may vary but this bears no relation to the eating quality. Stalks should be tender and firm with compact dark green or purplish-green buds in the head. Old, frequently tough broccoli, can be detected by yellow "flowers" visible inside the buds. The more yellow flowers you see, the less desirable it is.

Broccoli is another excellent source of Vitamin A, one-half cup, pressure cooked, yielding enough to meet one-half the average daily requirement.

It is available every month of the year, but since the plants thrive on cool weather, smallest supply is in July and August.

Use broccoli as soon as possible, store only briefly at 32° F. and 95% relative humidity.

Trim to portion size before cooking. Broccoli cooks well in a pressure cooker or, if boiling, try this system: place broccoli one-layer deep in a pan, pour boiling water over it and then cover with damp towel. The towel will help steam the stalks evenly as the water is kept boiling gently.

In cooking, use as little water as possible and rapid cooking. The fleshy stems of broccoli take longer to cook than the blossom. In general, the broccoli may be prepared similar to asparagus, with the stems standing in boiling, salted water and permitting the buds to be cooked by the steam created by the covered pan. Or, the broccoli may be cut in pieces and the stems cooked a short time before adding the blossoms. Rapid cooking and very little water tends to preserve the nutrients. Good sauces for broccoli include Hollandaise, mayonnaise, polonaise and Amandine.

BRUSSELS SPROUTS

Brussels sprouts look like miniature cabbages and are at their best between October and March. They receive their name from the Belgian city of Brussels, where they were first grown in the 13th Century.

Good sprouts are firm, compact, fresh, of bright appearance and good green color. Puffy or soft sprouts are usually poor in quality and flavor. Wilted or yellowing leaves indicate aging.

They are commonly not sold by varietal name. Size and color are more likely to be the best buying criteria.

Most supplies are produced in California, New York and Oregon. Available about ten months of the year, peak supplies are from October through December.

Use as soon as possible. For brief storage, hold at 32° F. and 90% relative humidity, to keep freshness and good green color.

Be sure the stem ends of the sprouts are not cut too closely during preparation or it will cause the outer leaves to fall off in cooking. Serve in a butter sauce, if boiled or steamed, or saute with sliced almonds for a specialty treatment. Some poppy seeds mixed into the butter sauce will produce still another tasty variation in service.

Raw brussels sprouts are rich in Vitamin C and B_1, but care must be exercised in cooking them to avoid loss of these elements. Prolonged boiling can destroy Vitamin C and also detract from the full flavor of brussels sprouts.

One cup provides 160% of the daily recommended allowance of Vitamin C, one-tenth of the Vitamin B_1 and one-tenth of the iron, for an adult.

Total U.S. production of these "baby cabbages" annually average close to 69 million pounds, of which about 19 million pounds is consumed fresh. Despite the fact this vegetable needs a long, cool growing season, can withstand considerable freezing temperatures, "Sunny California" produces more sprouts than all other states.

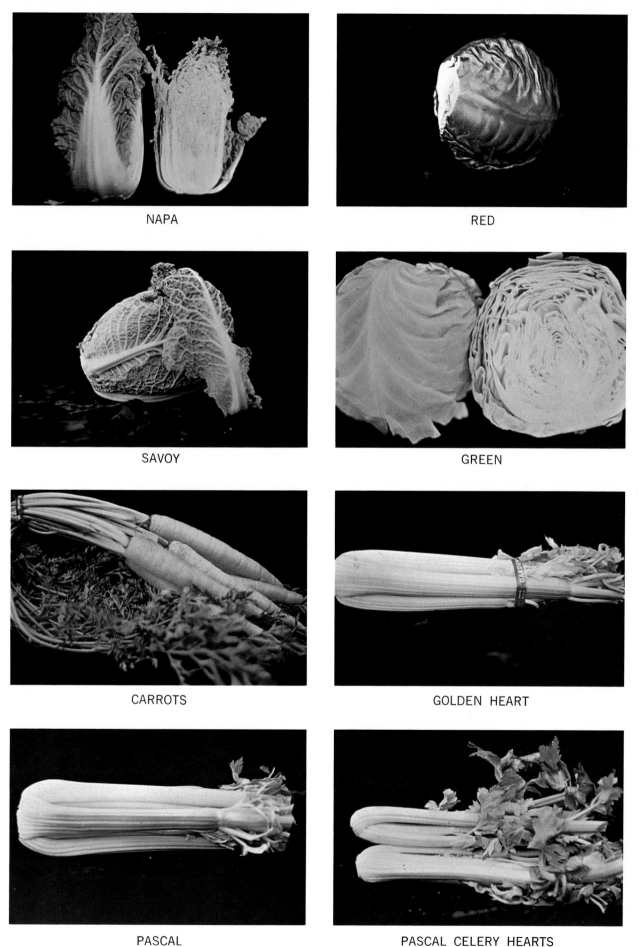

NAPA

RED

SAVOY

GREEN

CARROTS

GOLDEN HEART

PASCAL

PASCAL CELERY HEARTS

67

CABBAGE

Originally found wild on the seashores of Southern Europe, England and Denmark, the cabbage today is very extensively cultivated all over the world. It is interesting to note that several varieties of this vegetable were known as far back as the early days of Greece. In fact, from these original strains stem several of our present vegetables — brussels sprouts, cauliflower, kale and kohlrabi.

Despite its plentifulness, however, cabbage can be expensive if you do not pay attention to its careful selection. There are numerous common varieties but the quality characteristics are generally the same for all types.

Well-trimmed, reasonably solid heads that are heavy for their size and show no discolored veins, are your best buy. Early or new cabbage is not so firm as some of the Fall and Winter strains, which are suitable for storing.

One of the most unusual-appearing varieties is called Savoy cabbage. Its yellowish, crimped leaves form a head usually not much harder than that of Iceberg lettuce. Another novel type is Celery cabbage, also called Chinese cabbage, which has some of the characteristics of both Romaine and cabbage. This variety is used principally for salads and its long, oval-shaped head should be firm, fresh and well blanched.

Except for color, red cabbage is identical to other "headed" types.

Tests show that raw cabbage is rich in Vitamin C and has a fair content of Vitamin B_1. Like so many other vegetables, it also is a good source of several important minerals, and is low in calories.

Incidentally, here's a cooking hint. The typical cabbage odor can be appreciably decreased by dropping a whole walnut into the water in which this vegetable is cooked.

Cabbage stores well at 32° F. and 90% relative humidity, if well ventilated. It wilts quickly in dry storage.

The smaller the pieces, the faster cabbage will cook; and the faster it cooks, the better for flavor, as well as nutrition. Cut it into portion size before cooking. Shredded cabbage makes an excellent hot vegetable, in addition to being one of the top favorite raw salads (cole slaw). Marinate uncooked cole slaw in dressing for at least an hour and toss occasionally. Red cabbage makes a colorful accent to tossed lettuce salad. There is cabbage soup, stuffed cabbage, baked cabbage in egg casserole and cabbage with sour cream.

Annual available supply is fairly constant, every month of the year.

CARROTS

When carrots were first brought to England from Holland, stylish ladies used the feathery leaves to decorate their hair, and in Germany a substitute for coffee was made from carrots chopped into small pieces and browned.

Indians liked carrots so well, they would steal them from the early settlers' gardens, when they stole nothing else!

The carrot owes its chief claim of nutritional fame to the extraordinary amount of Vitamin A found in its roots. As a matter of fact, this vitamin is also termed "carotene" and ¾ of a cup of raw carrots can supply over twice the amount needed daily by the average person; 100 grams of edible portion has 11,000 units. Vitamin A improves vision, particularly at night, doctors tell us.

Brightly and good-colored carrots that have a well-shaped, firm flesh are best eating. Usually these are smooth, clean and free from straggling rootlets.

Carrots today are principally sold in a plastic-like bag. Science learned the carrot top draws moisture from the root and therefore carrots without tops will stay fresh longer than those with tops.

Principal states of production are California, Texas, Michigan. Some carrots grown in northern states and Canada are stored with their tops off. With favorable moisture and temperature control, they can be stored in good condition for many months. Ideal storage conditions are 32° F., relative humidity 95%.

Fresh carrots are an easy-to-prepare fresh vegetable. Wash, trim as necessary. "Shoestring" or carrot sticks can be the tastiest of carrot dishes. The flavor actually changes in this cut because there is a greater ratio of outside area to core material. Carrots Vichy (glazed in butter with chopped parsley) is another good method. Add whole carrots to the top of a pot roast as it is cooking, and they will take on the flavor of the meat.

Fresh carrots are on the market all year, with no distinct peak and with large supplies at all times. The carrot is of the parsley family, which includes also dill, caraway, coriander, anise, parsley, parsnips, celery and many others — about 2,500 species in all.

Raw carrots, per 100 grams, have 42 calories; cooked, 31 calories. Eaten raw, carrots are one of the important detergent vegetables helpful to dental health.

Carrots are unaffected by loss of nutrient value when properly stored. Carotene, precursor of Vitamin A, actually increased in a 20 week storage test, remained constant for the next 10 weeks.

SNO-BALL CAULIFLOWER

ORNAMENTAL OR INDIAN

YELLOW (CLIPPED)

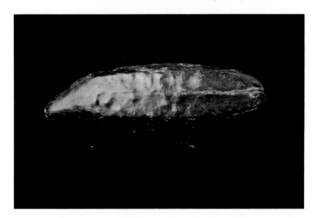

REGULAR CUCUMBER

LEMON CUCUMBER

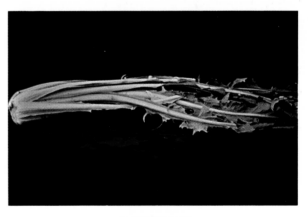

DANDELION

STANDARD EGGPLANT

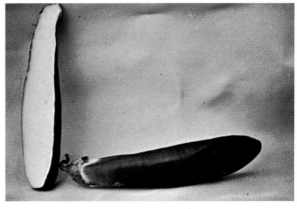

JAPANESE EGGPLANT

CAULIFLOWER

The word "cauliflower" comes from two Latin terms and literally means cabbage flower or stalk flower. Cauliflower is a cultivated descendant of common cabbage and has become an important crop in this country only since about 1920.

For years, the primary instructions for buying good cauliflower included the phrase, "Should wear a jacket of bright green, denoting freshness." Today, most cauliflower is shipped with the head only packaged in a clear-film wrap, thus eliminating the very perishable and heavy, ribbed leaves. The film helps to preserve freshness and nutrients, elimination of the heavily-ribbed leaves saves better than one-third the cost of shipping the product.

Regardless, there are still some sure signs in selecting good quality 'flower. Size of the head does not affect quality, nor do the tiny leaves you occasionally find growing through the curds; however, the small "flowers" in the head must not have started to grow, or the cauliflower will be inferior eating quality. It should not have a "ricy" appearance. The curd should be white, or only slightly creamy-white, very firm and compact. (Loose, open flower clusters indicate over-maturity.) Spotted, speckled or bruised curds should be avoided, unless this portion can be trimmed with little waste — and the curd meets all other requirements.

Aside from its mineral content, cauliflower in its raw state has a very high amount of Vitamins C and G, and is very low in calories.

Before cooking, soak it for about an hour with the head down in cold water, to which has been added a teaspoonful each of vinegar and salt. This will freshen the head and draw out any hidden, living, undesirables. This same treatment can be given to cabbage, sprouts and other vegetables.

Ideal storage temperature is 32° F., relative humidity 90%.

Avoid overcooking. When the stem end yields to the touch of the fork, boiled cauliflower is done. Buttered, creamed, au gratin and polonaise. Small bits of flowerettes are also used raw in salads and the vegetable is used in making soup.

Fresh cauliflower is one of the convenience vegetables. Almost all of it now comes to market stripped of ribs and leaves and ready for the pot.

Cauliflower is one of those white vegetables that can pick up an unattractive yellowish appearance if cooked in "hard" or alkaline water. Add a teaspoonful of fresh lemon juice to the water and the cauliflower will stay white.

Annual supply is fairly constant, but generally heavier September, October and November.

A new, green cauliflower variety is now commercially grown. A cross between conventional cauliflower and broccoli, it requires no hand tying in the field and will stay green through cooking. The curd (head) resembles cauliflower and is chartreuse green rather than dark green, such as broccoli. The new variety is higher in dry matter, cooks faster with less tendency to discolor, more tasty and less odoriferous while cooking.

CELERY

This vegetable is probably native to the Mediterranean Countries and was first cultivated in Italy and northern Europe for medicinal purposes only. Actual use as a food was first recorded in 1623 and for about 100 years thereafter, its food use was confined to flavorings.

There are two distinct types of celery . . . *Golden Heart,* which is bleached white, and *Pascal,* which is a dark, or light green, in color. The latter has practically replaced the former variety because of its distinctive flavor and almost complete lack of stringiness.

Quality characteristics for both varieties are the same. Leaf stems or stalks should be brittle enough to snap easily and of medium length and thickness. The inside of the stem should be smooth. If it feels rough or puffy to your finger, the celery is likely to be pithy. A good heart formation usually indicates good celery, and examining stalks for this feature will reveal whether there is any black heart, a rot very commonly found in stalks of celery. Leaflets should be fresh or only slightly wilted. Stalks of light green, glossy surface, will taste best.

Besides its appetizing flavor and taste, celery has a fair content of Vitamins A, B and G, as well as many helpful minerals. Eaten raw, it is one of the important detergent vegetables that can aid dental health.

Favorable storage temperature is 32° F., relative humidity 90-95%.

With only slight ingenuity, you will find every part of a stalk of celery is suitable for the table. The leaves are perfect for soups or broth. The outer ribs of the stalk are the ones best suited for cooked vegetables, either alone or with other products. It may be served creamed, braised (in chicken stock) or au gratin. The hearts are ideal for the relish tray. For a low calorie snack, you can't beat it, for a whole pound of celery has only 52 calories!

Available every month of the year, with principal supplies from California, Florida, Michigan and New York.

COLLARDS

Good quality collards are fresh, crisp, clean and free from insect injury. Wilting and yellowing of the leaves indicate age or other form of damage. They should have a healthy, green color, free of blemishes. Store at 32° F., 90% humidity. Crushed ice in the package of greens will help keep them fresh.

Closely related to kale, collards is one of the most primitive and oldest members of the Cabbage family. Georgia and Virginia have the largest acreages, but a good many other states also grow a large supply. They have been a favorite in the South for generations, where they are traditionally boiled with salt pork or hog jowls.

A pound of raw collards supplies 82 calories of food energy, heavy amounts of calcium, phosphorus, ascorbic acid, and better than 14,000 units of Vitamin A, as well as other elements and minerals.

Fry pieces of bacon or salt pork, then add clean, shredded collard leaves. Cover and simmer until tender; serve with lemon slices or vinegar. Cook collards *until just done* — about 10-15 minutes — and with *very little water.*

Supply is fairly constant throughout the year, heaviest period being January through April.

CORN

At one time, in Biblical days, all grain was called "corn". In England the British refer to our common corn as "maize", or Indian corn, to make the distinction apparent. It is a known fact that the aborigines, whom Columbus found in this land, were using corn long before his time. Many Indian legends were woven about this "all-inclusive food" which, in the days of the early settlers, had a mixture of red, white, yellow and black kernels in each ear. Careful breeding since then has produced the present-day refinements . . . giving us corn of all one color.

Sweet corn, which may be either white or yellow, is now an all-year-round food in the fresh form. There are over 200 varieties of sweet corn being grown in the U. S. The most important commercial varieties are yellow hybrids, with new varieties constantly being developed, having characteristics especially suited for an area of production. The retail store may call it "golden bantam" — but it *probably isn't* that variety! Generally the best, most properly developed corn, will be an even-numbered row of kernels — generally 12 to 14 row.

In best quality corn, the husk is a fresh green color while the kernels are tender, milky and sufficiently large to leave no space between the rows. They should be just firm enough to puncture rather easily when slight pressure is applied. Ears generally should be filled to the tip, with no rows of missing kernels. If you see cobs with kernels that are very soft and very small, you can be quite sure that the corn is immature.

Don't store it! The sooner it is used, the sweeter it will be! If necessary to store it, keep very cold and at very high humidity. The sugar in corn quickly turns to starch at higher temperatures. Common method of usage is boiling briefly (about 8 minutes). Instead of mere butter, add shredded parsley or chives to the butter to add a new effect.

Sweet corn is an agreeable contributor of carbohydrate and a variety of vitamins and minerals. Yellow varieties provide a fair amount of Vitamin A, along with Vitamin C, and other vitamins and minerals. It has only a trace of sodium.

Sweet corn is available in fresh form practically every month of the year, heaviest supplies from May to September. Winter supplies are grown in Florida and California.

CUCUMBERS

A good guide in buying cucumbers is to remember that those which are firm, fresh and with good green color, are best. The shade of color is important, as the older ones tend to be of rather dull green or sometimes yellow. Poor quality is also indicated by an outer rind that has a decided "give" to it when slight pressure is applied.

Florida, North Carolina, South Carolina, California are the leading producers. Washing or brushing, grading for size and defects, waxing the outer surface in central packing plants, have become common practices. Waxing (a harmless vegetable wax) is done to enhance appearance and to retard evaporation.

Cucumbers are divided into two classes, according to use — slicing (table) varieties and pickling varieties. This distinction is maintained even though slicing varieties may be used for both purposes; i.e., slices are often used for dills and large pickles. Pickling varieties produce numerous small, black-spined fruits. The fruits of most pickling varieties, while still immature, are so small they are not adapted for slicing. In general, the very small pickling cucumbers bring premium prices.

Cucumbers should be kept moderately cold, 45-50° F., at 85% relative humidity. They are an ideal accompaniment to summer meals. For raw eating, fresh cucumbers can be sliced or diced and added to a mixed salad. Cut lengthwise into sticks with the skin left on, they add color to a relish tray; peeled and sliced in sandwiches, served with vinegar, salt and pepper; or, sour cream. One prominent restaurant peels cucumbers and slices them lengthwise and calls them "icicles".

Generally grown in large fields, there is a very sizable hothouse production of cucumbers in Indiana, Iowa, Ohio, Michigan and other Central and mid-Western States.

"Cool as a cucumber" is not just a catchy phrase! In actual tests, on a hot day, the pulp temperature of a cucumber will be 20° cooler than the outside air.

Cucumbers can be a good snack for the weight watcher — only 55 calories per pound — an unpared cucumber (1#) contains heavy amounts of iron and Vitamin A, together with a wide variety of other elements and minerals. This is also one of the important detergent vegetables helpful to dental health.

The supply is generally good throughout the year, heaviest during the May through August period.

And now there's a seedless pickle! Very recently developed, the parthenocarpic (seedless) cucumber is still green, still has bumps on the skin, but will lend itself to mechanical harvesting, for the growth of the new cukes will be at the same rate, each plant.

DANDELION

This is a common, stemless plant of the sunflower family. They are believed to be native of Europe and Asia but are now found in most temperate countries. They have been used for food for centuries, but have been cultivated only within recent years.

Dandelions, when used as a food, usually are served as a salad green. However, cooked dandelion greens are an excellent source of Vitamin A, a half cup supplies more than enough of this element to meet the normal daily requirement.

Good quality is characterized by a fresh green appearance and comparatively large, tender leaves — if a portion of the root is still attached, they will probably be more succulent. Avoid dandelions which show excessive dirt, insects damage or are wilted, flabby and have yellow or tough leaves.

Store at 32° F., 90% relative humidity — preferably placing crushed ice in the container with the greens.

They top all other vegetables and fruits in iron and Vitamin A. One pound (raw) contains no refuse and provides 200 calories.

Dandelion is grown throughout the Southern and Southeastern seaboard States in large volume during the Spring and early summer months. Winter supply originates in Florida and California with annual supply each month fairly constant.

EGGPLANT

The origin of the eggplant is in subtropical or tropical India, as well as China. Fashionable Oriental ladies made a black dye with eggplant; the dye was used to stain teeth, then polished until they gleamed like metal.

Depending upon the variety, eggplant has a white, purple, purple-black, yellowish-white, red, or striped color. White is more prevalent in Europe, while the purple is more common in this country.

Purple eggplants should be of a clear, dark, glossy color that covers the entire surface. Heaviness and firmness of flesh are also important. Watch the size of eggplants you buy. A good rule to follow is to choose pear-shaped eggplants from three to six inches in diameter. Store only briefly at 45-50° F., 85% relative humidity.

Florida supplies about half the total production. Heaviest supplies are in August and September, lightest in February. Supplies are available all year.

Eggplant may be stuffed with meat or sauted in olive oil and cooked with plenty of tomato paste. It can be served as a substitute for meat; may be baked or broiled, scalloped, topped with cheese, cream mushrooms, sour cream. Small eggplants may be cooked whole or stuffed for individual servings, while large ones are good for stuffing or making casserole dishes.

Nutritionally, eggplant is not particularly famous for any one vitamin or mineral. It has a wide variety of these elements in varying amounts.

ENDIVE

Considerable confusion in using three terms has resulted throughout the country because of local misinterpretations of the exact vegetable to which they apply. For instance, endive is called escarole or chicory in some localities; chickory is misnamed endive, and so on. However, the descriptions and illustrations given here should facilitate your identification of each of these leafy greens.

Curly endive grows in a bunchy head with narrow, ragged-edge leaves which curl at the ends. The center of the head is a yellowish white and has a milder taste than the darker green outer leaves, which tend to be slightly bitter. If this center is not so white as desired when the endive is purchased, it can be further bleached by covering overnight with a damp cloth.

There is another variety of endive with broad leaves (Batavian endive) that do not curl at the tips. It is this type which is almost universally marketed as *escarole*.

Witloof chicory is a rather tightly folded plant that grows upright in a thin, elongated stalk, rather than flat or bushy like endive or escarole. This vegetable is usually bleached a decided white while growing and is known far more commonly as French endive than by its true botanical name.

Another form of chicory is grown for its large roots, which are dried and used as a supplement for coffee.

In buying, look for freshness, crispness, tenderness and a good green color of outer leaves, avoiding those heads with brownish or yellowish discolorations.

As is true of most leafy green vegetables, endive, escarole and chicory are all good sources of Vitamin A and also have a fair content of B_1, C and G. Used raw, they are part of the detergent vegetables so helpful for dental health.

Hold briefly at 32° F., relative humidity 90%. It keeps better with crushed ice in or around the package.

The leafy forms of these vegetables are used raw in a salad or cooked as greens. The Witloof type is used raw as a salad. When cooking, simmer them gently until tender in a tightly covered pan. Endive, Chicory and Escarole can be used in endless combinations with other greens and with any type of dressing.

GARLIC

Closely allied to the onion, garlic has been described as the "atomic bomb of the vegetable world". It is a member of the lily family and can point to a very distinguished background. It is a native of Western Asia and the Mediterranean, has been in cultivation for centuries.

It is a bulbous-rooted perennial plant. The root is a compound bulb consisting of several smaller sections, or cloves, which are enveloped by a common skin or membrane. It differs from the onion by being more powerful in its effects and more distinctive in its taste.

Garlic should be stored dry, away from onions and potatoes, preferably in a cool, dark area.

Garlic may form a part of almost any dish. It is used mainly to flavor meats, vegetables, stews, soups, salads, dressings, tomato dishes, spaghetti, sauces, and in the preparation of pickles and sausages.

An English writer claims that in India garlic has been a favorite for centuries for "improving the voice, intellect, complexion and promoting the union of fractured bones and helping to cure nearly all the ills that flesh is heir to". (We don't endorse these claims!)

Unless garlic is kept in a closed jar, its strong, pungent odor penetrates all food close to it. Because of this, many progressive grocers sell garlic from which the tops have been removed, handily packaged in small cellophane bags containing four or five segments.

A medium-sized bulb contains about 74% water, 20% carbohydrate and small amounts of protein, fat, ash and fiber. There are 450 calories per pound.

KALE

Grown extensively in Virginia, Maryland and New York, kale is native to the Eastern Mediterranean or to Asia Minor. These cabbage-like plants have been cultivated so long that origin is not definite.

Kale is a large, hardy, curly-leafed green, inexpensive and usually abundant throughout the winter. Dark green kale is best but a few leaves with slightly browned edges are not objectionable, as they can readily be trimmed. Leaves should be crisp, clean and free from bruising or crushing. Should be kept cold and moist. Do not plan to store for any length of time but, if necessary, hold at 40° F., with very high humidity.

To prepare kale, cut off and discard root ends, tough stems and discolored leaves. Cut off and discard midribs. Wash, lift out of water and shake the leaves well — do not use soda in cooking, as it makes kale mushy and destroys the Vitamin C. There are many uses — raw or cooked.

On the nutritional side, kale can lay claim to an impressive list of health-giving food qualities. Properly cooked, one-half cup will supply twice the normal daily need for Vitamin A, while experiments with this vegetable in its raw state show it is exceptionally rich in Vitamin C as well. Because it is low in calories, too, kale makes an excellent addition to any dinner menu.

LETTUCE

Lettuce is believed to be native to the Mediterranean and Near Eastern centers of origin of cultivated plants. Although lettuce has been cultivated for more than 2500 years, it is neither so old, nor was it so widely grown in prehistoric times, as a number of other garden crops.

Lettuce is generally grouped into five classes: *crisphead* (usually, but incorrectly, called Iceberg); *butterhead; Cos* or *romaine; looseleaf* or *bunching;* and *stem*.

The term "iceberg" has come to be applied to crisphead lettuce, but actually, Iceberg is the botanical name applied to a variety with red-tinged leaves and of no commercial importance. Nevertheless, for all practical purposes, "iceberg" now means to the public, Crisphead. This is by far the most popular and widely known variety of lettuce.

CHICORY ENDIVE

FRENCH ENDIVE

ESCAROLE

CLOVE GARLIC

WHITE GARLIC

MUSTARD

TURNIP

KALE

BUTTER LEAF LETTUCE

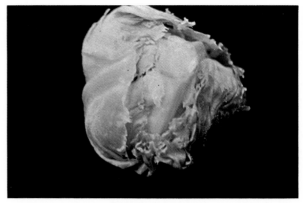

HEAD LETTUCE

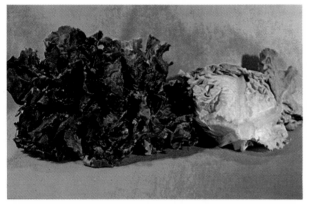

RED LEAF LETTUCE

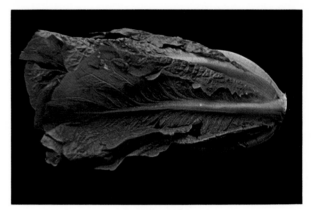

ROMAINE

SALAD LETTUCE

MUSHROOMS

CHIVES

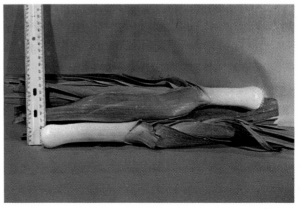

LEEK

The crisphead varieties are distinguished by their firm heads and brittle texture. The veins are coarse and the ribs fairly prominent; heads are usually six inches in diameter. Crisphead is the most important commercial type of lettuce in this country.

When making your selection, look for heads that are firm, compact — free from burned or rusty looking tips, along with general fresh appearance. The "hard as a rock" heads will probably be less sweet and tender than the "firm-not hard" rule used by lettuce industry experts.

The butterhead varieties are distinguished by their soft, pliable leaves and delicate buttery flavor. The veins are finer and the ribs less prominent than those of the crisphead varieties. Principal varieties of butterhead lettuce are Big Boston, White Boston, Bibb and May King.

Big Boston, sometimes called "Butterhead", is another rather well-known variety of lettuce, particularly in the East and Southeast. This type forms heads somewhat softer and lighter than Iceberg and not so crisp in texture; Boston lettuce is not as sweet and tender as other butterhead varieties, medium in size with light green outer leaves and light yellow leaves inside.

Bibb lettuce received its name from Major John Bibb, who was born in Virginia in 1789. They migrated to Russellville, Kentucky, where he spent the rest of his life experimenting with plants in the garden and greenhouse. John Bibb developed this small, cup-shaped lettuce, which has a distinct color, flavor and crispness. The leaves are a deep, rich, green and blend into a whitish green towards the core. Quality is excellent — with a delicate, buttery flavor, sweet, tender. Grown principally in greenhouses, it is erroneously referred to as "limestone". The flavor is best described as "distinctly lettuce with a touch of cultivated Dandelion or Italian Chicoria flavor".

Cos, or romaine, grown mainly in the East and South, has a long, loaf-shaped head and long, narrow leaves. The varieties of Cos are divided into self-closing and loose-closing types. The leaves appear coarse, but they are tender, sweet and tasty and have less bitterness than other varieties. Has dark green outer leaves and golden-yellow inner ones, and stronger flavor than Iceberg.

Leaf lettuce, as the name implies, grows with leaves loosely branching from its stalk — these varieties do not form heads. The leaves are clustered or pressed together but only the young ones at the center of the plant overlap to any extent. Leaf lettuce has a crisp texture preferred by many people.

The edible part of stem lettuce is the enlarged stem or seedstalk. It may be peeled and eaten raw or it may be boiled, stewed, or creamed. Stem lettuce is an ingredient of many Chinese dishes. Celtuce is the only variety offered for sale in the United States.

Corn salad, a lettuce-like vegetable, is also known as lamb's lettuce or fetticus. Its leaves are generally used in the fresh state but are also sometimes cooked as greens.

Vacuum-cooling of crisphead lettuce at shipping point has created a revolutionary change in the handling of lettuce. The process permits the use of any type of container for packaging lettuce, providing the container admits ventilation. The principle of vacuum-cooling has long been known. Evaporative cooling was utilized early in the history of man to cool water. Today, the pulp temperature of lettuce is quickly cooled to 32-34° F. by placing individual cartons (or even whole carloads of cartons) of lettuce in large, metal "tubes". Mechanically, a vacuum is immediately created and within 28-30 minutes the pulp temperature of the lettuce is drawn down to the above temperatures. Weight losses during the cooling process are small.

Crisphead lettuce should be cored before washing so the cleansing spray of water can run between the lower leaves to rinse out any stray sand. To core a head of lettuce, hold the head core-end down and whack it onto the kitchen counter. Then simply twist and lift out the core with your fingers. After washing, shake the washed lettuce vigorously to remove all water possible, then turn cored end down on paper towels to drain thoroughly. After draining, mop up any moisture that fails to evaporate and store in the refrigerator in a bowl with an airtight lid, or, a plastic bag. Lettuce can be kept two or three weeks if stored at 32° F., assuming it was in good condition prior to storing.

Lettuce is congenial with all fruits and vegetables and contributes a useful amount of Vitamin A, Vitamin C, iron, calcium, as well as other vitamins and minerals. Boston and Bibb varieties are high in iron. Use it as the basis for healthful salads of limitless variety; adding lettuce to a sandwich not only makes it more palatable, but improves digestion. Raw lettuce is one of the important detergent foods, so helpful to dental health. Only 32 calories in a 4-inch head.

TIP: For lettuce so crisp it crackles, give a plastic-bagged head of iceberg a super-chilling in the freezer for a *few* minutes before you serve it. Or, prepare your salad bowl with a variety of greens, place it in the freezer for a few minutes, add dressing and your family and friends will rave about the crisp tastiness of your salad! And for the *really* memorable salad, place salad forks in the refrigerator several hours ahead of your serving — or place them in the freezer section for a few minutes (with your salad).

MUSHROOMS

It was formerly believed that darkness was required for growing good mushrooooms. Scientists say this is not true; mushrooms need proper compost, good sanitation, and most of all, a constant and suitable temperature and protection against drafts. In many parts of the world, such as Thailand and Japan, mushrooms are grown outdoors; however, the climate in the U. S. is not suitable for the commercial production of mushrooms out of doors. Therefore, in some areas of the Eastern United States, as well as France, they are grown in natural caves or cultured in carefully designed, windowless buildings in which temperature, humidity and ventilation are precisely controlled.

Freshness, color and shape are the three points generally considered in buying mushrooms. Variety is not a factor, since all of the cultivated mushrooms on the U. S. market are of the same variety.

Avoid withered mushrooms, since this is a sign of age. Mushrooms which look bright and attractive in the store can be kept in the home refrigerator for 4-5 days with little effect. All mushrooms, however, will eventually oxidize and turn dark. This will occur very quickly when exposed to room temperature, but more slowly when refrigerated. An open "veil" around the base of the cap is also a sign of old age.

Normal color is white to pallid brown; however, a darkened or spotted mushroom is not necessarily spoiled, but instead, may be bruised. The cap is more tender than the stem. The size of mushrooms is not a reliable indication of whether they are tender.

Because they are so widely relished as the "finishing touch" to a sizzling beefsteak, mushrooms find a ready sale in most food stores. They are extremely versatile, adding exciting flavor and texture to meat, poultry and seafood. Cheese and eggs, too, team well with mushrooms. Fresh mushrooms are available throughout the year, with peak in November and December and low point in August. In any of their available forms, they are considered an easily prepared, convenience food.

First rule in preparing mushrooms for cooking is: *do not peel*. Much of the flavor and nutritive value of the mushroom is in the skin. If the bottom of the stem looks dry and brown, trim away a thin slice and discard. Other than that, you should find a good use for every bit of the mushrooms you buy. Do not wash mushrooms roughly. All they need is rinsing in cool water, jiggling them about a few times and then blotting with a towel. Do not soak. In fact, we suggest washing only those you are about to use. Refrigerate until ready for use, preferably in the tray in which they were purchased, covered lightly. Cook mushrooms briefly, no more than 4-5 minutes. If you want to retain mushroom texture and flavor in a stew, gravy or sauce, etc., add the mushrooms four minutes before taking the food off the heat. If, however, you want the mushroom flavor to mingle with that of the accompanying items, add them at the same time as you do all the other ingredients. Do not overcook — this will dry out the mushrooms and make them tough.

Mushrooms can be frozen by adding ½ tsp. salt and lemon juice to 1 qt. boiling water. Add the washed mushrooms to the water and return to boil; cook three minutes. Rinse mushrooms in cold water, drain and pat dry. Seal in plastic bags and freeze. Will keep for months.

Mushrooms are low in sodium and are recommended for special diets. Contain only 90 calories per pound, while their satiety value gives the dieter a sense of having eaten well. Provide a relatively good source of protein, phosphorus, iron, and other minerals.

MUSTARD GREENS

Mustard greens are among the minor leafy vegetables. There are no production and consumption figures; however, approximately 30 million pounds are used annually! They are especially popular in the South and may be found in all markets almost any time of the year.

Mustard greens are grown commercially mainly in the South, but also in California, Michigan, Ohio, Indiana, New Jersey and Arizona. The species most often grown for commercial production is known as *leaf mustard*. A species grown in home gardens is called *mustard spinach* or *tendergreen mustard*. Seeds of various species can be used to make the mustard that goes on the hot dog and hamburger. The large-leaved, fancy, pungent garden mustards grown in this country as potherbs are generally the brown or Indian mustard. They are grown mainly in California and the Pacific Northwest for their seeds.

Mustard greens should be fresh, tender, crisp and of a good, green color. Wilted, dirty, discolored or spotted leaves are indications of poor condition and quality. The presence of seed stems is a sure indication of age and toughness. In buying, the smaller leaves, 6-12″ long, are preferred. The young, tender leaves of Mustard Greens can be used as salad leaves, either alone or mixed with other salad greens. The older, tender leaves are used for cooking and should be handled in similar fashion to other herbs. Only the water clinging to the leaves after washing should be used.

Greens need to be prepared from the moment you buy them to bring them out at their crispest, freshest best. Wash them as soon as you bring them in from the market. Shake off as much water as possible, then spread loose leaves on paper towels to dry. They should be cooled as near 32° F. as possible and kept at or near that temperature until used. Humidity should be high, 90-95%. If temperature is kept low and humidity high, leafy greens have a shelf life of 10-14 days. Vitamin content and quality are retained when wilting is prevented. Tests have shown that within 24 hours, without refrigeration, Mustard Greens will lose 20% of their Vitamin C and will begin to wilt.

A cupful of cooked Mustard Greens provides 61% more than the recommended daily allowance of Vitamin A for an adult; more than the entire allowance of Vitamin C; a fifth of the iron, as well as a useful amount of other vitamins and minerals, including folic acid. There are only 35 calories in a cooked cupful.

OKRA

Because of the outstanding popularity of okra in the French cookery of Louisiana, it is assumed that it was introduced to this country by the French colonists of Louisiana in the early 1700's.

On the market all year, it is used principally in soups, although in the South it is also cooked and eaten by itself as any other vegetable. The young, tender pods of okra, popular in "Creole" cookery, are excellent in soups and stews. It may be boiled, baked or fried. Okra combines well with other vegetables, especially with tomatoes, and is a natural thickening agent, performing this function in gumbos.

Proper cooking will overcome the pastiness not always suited to American taste. Also, pastiness will not occur if the whole pods are not broken or subjected to long cooking. Whether boiled, baked or fried, rapid cooking will preserve the flavor as well as prevent the mucilaginous consistency from developing.

It should not be cooked in iron, copper, or brass utensils, for the resulting chemical reaction, while harmless, will cause the pods to become discolored.

Good quality okra may be green or white in color, with pods that are either long and thin or short and chunky. In all cases, freshness can be determined by the tenderness of the pods — those that snap easily or puncture on slight pressure being best. Young, tender, fresh, clean pods of small-to-medium size, ranging from

2-4 inches in length, usually are of good quality. Pods that have passed their prime will present a somewhat dull, dry appearance. It can be stored a maximum of 2 weeks at 50° F., and 85-95% relative humidity.

There are 130 calories in a pound of raw okra, as well as more than one-half the recommended daily dietary allowance of Vitamin A, plus twice the rda of Vitamin C. Also contains some amounts of protein, calcium, phosphorus, iron, thiamine, niacin.

ONIONS

The onion is another vegetable which has been known and used for many centuries. In fact, the onion has been known and cultivated as an article of food from the earliest period of history. In general, they are on the market all year in large quantity.

Basically, on the American market, there are three types of "dry" onions: the early Bermuda-Granex-Grano; the late crop onions; and the Creole type.

The Bermuda-Granex-Grano type are flat to top-shaped, with varying amounts of intermediate shapes. These onions belong to the group considered "early maturing" or "short day". The granex is probably the most widely grown short-day onion, due to its attractiveness and productiveness. The bulbs have thin, yellow scales, flesh medium-firm, exceptionally mild in flavor and crisp. The Yellow Bermuda is another of the short-day variety. The bulbs are flat and flesh soft and mild. Storage life is short. Both of these may be yellow or white skinned.

The late or main crop onions are mostly of the globe type and have distinctly yellow, white or red skins. Yellow globe is a commercial term applied to several varieties and strains.

The Yellow Sweet Spanish is strictly a "long-day" onion adapted to the more northern districts of the semi-arid irrigated regions of the Western U. S. The large bulbs are globe-shaped, the dry scales are dark-yellow and adhere fairly well. The necks are fairly heavy with the flesh medium firm and mild. Sweet Spanish onions, originally introduced from Spain, are produced in large quantities.

Red varieties are from the Creole family and usually a strong-flavored onion; however, pungency is not entirely related to variety, since it has been found that the same variety can have considerably different flavor when grown in different locations and on different soils.

Onions of any of the above varieties are often called "boilers" when they range from 1-1½ inches in diameter. Any which are still smaller than that are termed "picklers".

OKRA

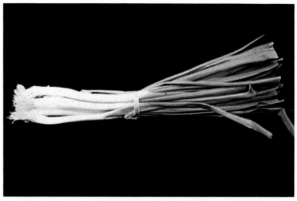

GREEN ONIONS

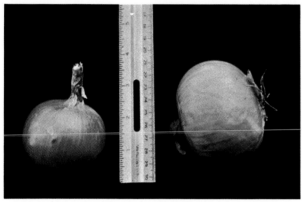

JUMBO YELLOW

RED

WHITE

EASTERN SHALLOTS

PARSLEY

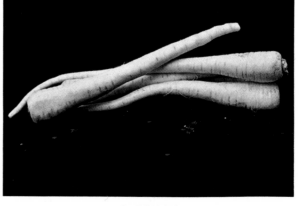

PARSNIPS

When selecting dry onions, look for those that are well shaped and dry enough to crackle. Thin necks and bright, hard bulbs are two other indications of quality. Avoid those with a wet, soggy feeling at the neck, as this is usually, although not invariably, a sign that decay is starting, if not already present. Size has nothing to do with quality.

Green onions are merely onions that are harvested green. Many like to munch the tops, as well as the small bulb. Sometimes the greens are chopped and mixed with cottage cheese. Often green onions are cut up and put in salad. They may also be boiled and served like asparagus. In selecting, they should have good, green-colored tops and white, bleached stems up to about three inches from the roots.

The *shallot*, sometimes called "scallion", belongs to the same group as onions, leek, chives, garlic. This group is one of the oldest, having been known for many thousands of years. Many persons confuse shallots with green onions, scallions or leeks. Green onions have a definite bulb formation; *scallions* are any shoots from the white onion varieties that are pulled before the bulb has formed; while *leeks* are similar in appearance to scallions, but have flat leaves and the white stalk has a diameter of about 1½″ and is 6-8″ in length. The shallot can be distinguished from these others by its distinctive bulbs, which are made up of cloves, like garlic. *Chives* are tiny onions whose roots and tops are both used for flavoring, generally sold in pots, all green, and are pencil-lead thin.

For "dry" onions, cold storage is not essential, but dry storage is desirable, with a 70-75% relative humidity. At higher humidities, onions are subject to root growth and decay in time. They should never be stored with potatoes, for example, because they will take on moisture from the potatoes and decay quickly.

Medium "dry" onions are good for chopping, boiling, stuffing. Large Yellow are all-purpose, but excellent for stuffing and slicing for hamburgers. Jumbo onions are excellent for hamburgers and French fried onion rings. Red onions are good mainly for salads and other garnishes where rings are used, since the outside is the only part that is red.

Onions are used as a main vegetable dish or as a flavorful addition to the main meat dish. They are good boiled, broiled, baked, creamed, steamed, fried, french fried, roasted, pickled, in soups and stews, for onion rings, sliced raw and diced raw in salads. In fact, there are very few recipes, other than desserts, which do not include at least a suspicion of onion!

They are low in calories, with one raw onion (approximately 2½″ in diameter) providing only 40 calories. A cup of cooked onions provides about one-fourth of the daily recommended allowance of ascorbic acid. Raw, they are one of the detergent foods suggested as an aid to dental health.

Peeling: To help keep your eyes from watering when you're peeling onions, try holding a crust of bread between your teeth with one end projecting outward. Pouring scalding water over onions before you begin peeling will also help prevent this annoyance, as will peeling them under water.

Odors: These can be removed from a knife by running it through a raw potato. If you have onion odors on your hands, try rubbing them briskly with celery salt before washing. If you don't want your breath to reek of onions, try eating a half-dozen sprigs of parsley, which have been dipped in salt or vinegar.

Polishing: Rubbing tin objects strongly with a raw onion should give them a sparkling new polish. You can also shine brass ornaments by using a soft cloth which has been dipped in the juice of a boiled onion.

PARSLEY

Parsley is not only a sprightly garnish on a steak platter, or mild seasoning, but a food in its own right.

It is a native of the Mediterranean shores, has been used as an herb and garnish for thousands of years.

Today, parsley grows both in the U. S., as well as several European countries. It is exceptionally high in Vitamins A and C. Although the curly leaf variety is the most popular, the flat leaf, sometimes called Italian parsley, also is grown and used in the U. S.

Like other greens, they keep best at low temperatures, 32° F., and high humidity. Use of crushed ice is desirable in keeping parsley.

The most frequent use is as a garnish and should be bright green and fresh-looking to be completely effective. Chopped parsley should be folded into a towel and wrung out thoroughly so that it dries out quickly. Besides as a garnish for meats, it may be a dominant seasoning for soups, bisques, bread spread and a sauce in these recipes. Use it chopped or shredded in butter—for bread or sweet corn.

In selecting parsley, look for a healthy all-over green, preferably dark, with no yellowing, for the latter is an indication of age. It should be crisp and firm. Particularly for the more popular curly parsley, it should spring back with a slight pressure between your fingers or fist. Black, watery areas indicate bruising.

Annual supply each month is fairly constant, slightly heavier the last three months of the year. Parsley is one of the detergent foods recommended to assist in dental health!

FRESNO CHILI

JALAPENO CHILI

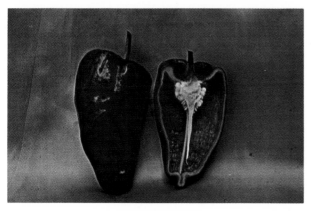

PASILLA CHILI

SERRANO CHILI

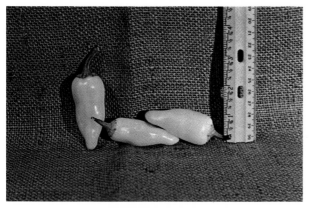

YELLOW CHILI

HOT CHILI

CHILI PODS

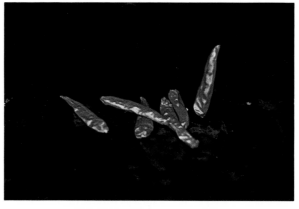

JAPANESE RED CHILI (DRY)

PARSNIPS

Parsnips are one of the hardiest vegetables on the market and hold up well under either warm or quite cold temperatures. However, many authorities state that the parsnip's flavor is not really brought out until it has been stored for some time at a temperature close to 32°. Small-to-medium-size parsnips are usually the best quality, provided they are firm and well shaped. The jumbo sizes are likely to have a "woody" core. They should be free of straggly rootlets and fairly smooth.

Best temperature for storage is 32° F., relative humidity 90%. They wilt readily under dry conditions. Stews, soups and mashed probably offer the best potentials for service. They are delicious when creamed or sauteed or deep fat fried in thin slices in batter. When properly cooked (steamed, not boiled), parsnips have a sweet, nutty flavor.

One pound of raw parsnips is fairly high in Vitamin A, phosphorus, iron, sodium, potassium and a fair amount of other Vitamins and minerals; also has 293 calories. Annual supply is fairly constant, lightest in the four months beginning in May.

PEPPERS

Peppers, which are believed to have originated in South America, are available on the market the year around. Peppers of one kind or another are eaten all over the world. In the United States, however, the sweet, mild pepper is usually preferred and may be bought either green or red, according to the stage of maturity desired.

Best quality peppers are well-shaped, thick walled and firm, with a uniform glossy color. Pale color and soft seeds are signs of immaturity, while sunken blister-like spots on the surface indicate that decay may set in rather quickly.

The varieties of garden peppers may be classified in two categories: those with mild or sweet fleshed fruit, and those with hot or pungent-fleshed fruits. Within each of these groups is a remarkable range of sizes, shapes and colors of fruits. The *California Wonder,* or *Bell,* are the most popular because of highly desirable size, shape and attractiveness.

Chili, Pimiento, and *Cayenne* are varieties of hot peppers which are often dried and sold in strings. Pimiento peppers are canned extensively for use in preparing such foods as pimiento cheese and the red stuffing for olives. Paprika is the finely ground fruit walls of paprika peppers, a mild type.

Mature-green peppers should not be stored at temperatures below 45° F., and the ideal temperature is about 46-48°, with relative humidity of 85%. Under the most favorable conditions, peppers can be stored successfully for only 12-15 days.

Red Sweet peppers are sometimes diced and mixed with sweet corn or other vegetables. The Red Sweet pepper is a rich green before changing colors.

Green Sweet peppers are delicious stuffed and baked. They are delicious, too, fried Italian style — in olive oil flavored with a noticeable bit of crushed garlic. Additionally, sweet peppers are canned or pickled in brine for use in salads or other foods. They are also french fried, used in soups and stews. They are good boiled, plain or with other vegetables.

Low in calories — one medium raw pepper contains about 15 calories, they are remarkably high in Vitamin C. One medium *raw* provides more than the recommended daily allowance of Vitamin C for an adult, and one medium-sized *cooked* provides almost the entire daily allowance of Vitamin C for an adult. They also supply some Vitamin A and a variety of other vitamins and minerals, plus bulk desirable for good digestion.

Garden peppers — hot and mild types — are not related to the pepper, from which we get black pepper.

Annual supply is fairly constant, but heaviest during the late Spring and Summer months. Winter supply is grown principally in California, Florida and Texas, with many Southern, Midwest and Eastern States growing summer supplies. Raw green peppers are another detergent food recommended as an aid to dental health.

POTATOES

The potato is the world's most important vegetable and is one of the very few that originated in the Western hemisphere, probably in the Andean region of South America. In Chile, found many years ago growing wild, the species found there more resembles the varieties we know today, in contrast to those tubers found in Peru, Bolivia and Ecuador.

The word "potato" apparently came from the Spanish "patata" or "batata", which was applied to sweet potatoes, and, by mistake, to the white potato. Botanically, it is a succulent, non-woody annual plant of the nightshade family. Few of the latter are of economic importance, except the cultivated eggplant.

A great many people are misinformed about white or Irish potatoes on two counts. First, they are *not* native to Ireland, and were *not* introduced to the Irish until 1585. Second, white potatoes, contrary to popular belief, are not an exceptionally fattening food. As a

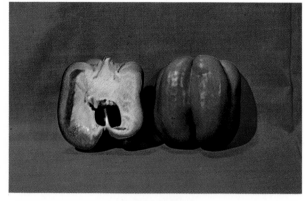

GREEN BELL

CALIF. WONDER

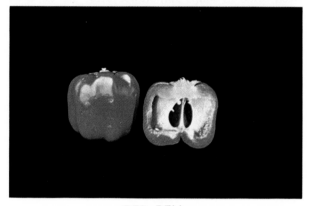

RED BELL

matter of fact, one medium-size potato contains no more calories than a large apple or a single baking powder biscuit of average size.

Furthermore, the potato is a fair source of Vitamins B₁, C and G and, in addition, has an abundant content of iron, phosphorus and other minerals. With such a wealth of food values, it is therefore obvious that potatoes more than deserve their position as the backbone of the world's vegetable diet!

Potatoes are processed into an important array of food products, expanding at a very rapid rate in recent years as a result of the trend towards "convenience" foods.

A large part of the U.S. potato crop must be stored, since most of it is harvested in September to November. Storage is generally done on the farm or at a controlled air storage of an association or corporation. Potatoes are generally held in common storage rather than cold storage. In storing potatoes, temperature maintained in the storage is dependent a great deal on ultimate use intended. For general fresh use, outside winter air permits fan injection into the storage area to maintain optimum storage temperatures with moderate air circulation.

Early or "new" potatoes are shipped directly from

the field after harvesting. On occasions, they are excessively "skinned" or "feathered" because of immaturity, coupled with rough handling. The feathered area is likely to turn brown or black, causing the potato to wilt or shrivel at normal room temperatures. While there is much consumer preference for new potatoes, don't plan to home-store them for more than a few days.

Much experimentation has been made by use of gamma rays to inhibit sprouting of potatoes. Government tests have shown that by such radiation they can completely inhibit the sprouting of potatoes to preserve for future use; however, at this writing, there are no commercial installations for this method because of cost.

Use of the chemical sprout inhibitors on the fall crop is increasing. This may be applied to the potatoes as a gas or dust at the time of placement in storage, or in the wash water as they are withdrawn from storage. These inhibitors are harmless and do not change the color, taste or texture of the food.

The "greening" on the surface of the skin of a potato is a result of development of chlorophyl in potatoes that have been exposed to either sunlight or artificial light. While most people believe this green area on the skin is a result of something happening in the field, generally speaking it is the result of overhead lights in the display area at the retail store.

When storing in the home, it is best to store in a cool, dry, dark area, as greening takes place more rapidly at room temperature than in a cool area. The affected potatoes have a bitter taste.

Throughout the world, potato tubers are of a great many sizes, shapes and colors. The flesh color may be white, yellow, pink, red or blue — but only the white-fleshed types are acceptable in the U.S.

Per capita U.S. consumption of fresh potatoes has declined from a high of 184 lbs. in 1910 to a recent 94-96 lbs. Economic studies reveal several reasons, among which is *the "fattening" misconception,* the greater variety of other vegetables offered at retail level and alleged convenience of the processed product. Also, current practices of the consumer buying in small quantities (10 lbs. and less) may mean less waste, which contributes to the decline in the total fresh quantity used; however, total U.S. potato consumption, all forms, remains at a high 101-118 lbs. per capita, most of this wide variation a result of price, the latter mostly dependent on the size of the crops produced.

At every level of potato marketing, potatoes are identified by a grade, the most popular being U.S. #1, although this is not the best U.S. grade for this product. When buying, look them over carefully to make certain they satisfy your own specifications.

In the industry, potatoes are generally classified in five basic types: the *Round White, Russet Burbank* (long Russet group), *Russet Rural* or *Round Russet, Round Red* group and the *Long White.*

Each variety listed here was developed for specific, or perhaps general, home or commercial use, as shown. Unfortunately, the seed used, climate under which the tubers were grown, amount of water and fertilizer, the temperature and humidity of the storage prior to shipment — all have an effect on cooking qualities. But using the following guide, in combination with variety marked on the consumer size unit purchased, or shown in the bulk display, should serve your purpose:

CHEROKEE, short, elliptical, frequently flattened area on one side toward stem end, medium shallow eyes and white flesh. Good for boiling, baking.

CHIPPEWA, elliptical to oblong, shallow eyes with white skin; ideal for boiling with no darkening after cooking.

COBBLER (Irish), roundish with white, smooth skin and shallow to rather deep eyes; best for boiling, may be baked; darkens after cooking.

GREEN MOUNTAIN, oblong, broad, flattened with smooth, sometimes netted, white skin and medium deep eyes. Good for boiling, baking; flesh generally darkens after cooking.

HUNTER, elliptical, medium thick, skin smooth, dark cream buff; eyes shallow, moderately well distributed; white flesh. Good for boiling or baking with no darkening after cooking.

KATAHDIN, tubers are short elliptical to round, medium thick with shallow eyes and smooth, white skin. Ideal for boiling, slight darkening after cooking; also used for French Fries.

KENNEBEC, elliptical to oblong with shallow eyes, white skin and flesh; good for boiling, baking, French Fries; generally no darkening after cooking.

KESWICK, elliptical to oblong tubers with eyes medium in depth; dark cream skin color with white flesh; good for boiling, baking, with no discoloration after cooking.

McCLURE, RED, entire supply from San Luis Valley of Colorado; tubers generally medium size, round, flattened, skin sometimes somewhat netted, red. Eyes few, mostly at seed end, very shallow except bud-eye cluster, which is frequently depressed.

NORGOLD RUSSET, oblong to long, heavy netting to skin, uniform russetting; shallow eyes, very well distributed. Good for boiling or French Fries; no darkening after cooking.

NORLAND, oblong, smooth red skin and shallow eyes with white flesh. Ideal for boiling with no darkening of skin.

PUNGO, elliptical, somewhat rounded tubers with white, flaked skin, medium deep eyes and white flesh. Good for boiling and baking with no skin discoloration.

RED LaSODA, semi-round to slightly oblong with bright, red skin, very smooth. Eyes are medium in depth to shallow. Ideal for boiling, no darkening after cooking.

RED PONTIAC, round to oblong with smooth or sometimes netted, intense red skin, medium deep eyes and white flesh. Ideal for boiling. Slight darkening after cooking.

RUSSET BURBANK (Netted Gem), long, cylindrical or slightly flattened with russetted, heavy-netted skin and numerous, well distributed shallow eyes and white flesh. Good for every purpose but ideal for baking and French Fries. Slight discoloration after cooking.

SEBAGO, elliptical to round, with smooth, white skin and shallow eyes; good for boiling, baking, with no darkening after cooking.

WHITE ROSE (Long White), large, long, elliptical, flattened tubers with smooth, white skin and numerous medium-deep eyes with white flesh. Ideal for boiling, generally no darkening after cooking.

WHITE ROSE

RED PONTIAC

RUSSET BURBANKS

KATAHDIN

KENNEBEC

GREEN MOUNTAIN

NORLAND

CHEROKEE

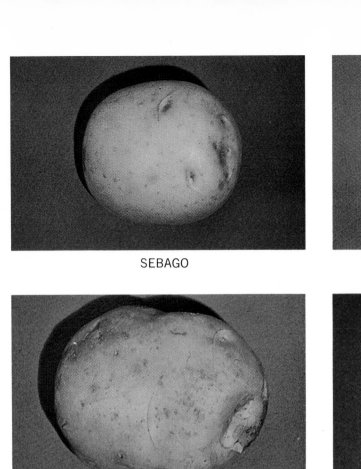

SEBAGO

KESWICK

CHIPPEWA

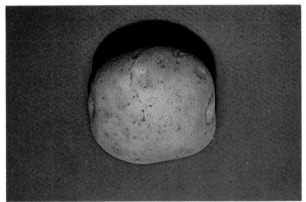

HUNTER

NORGOLD RUSSET

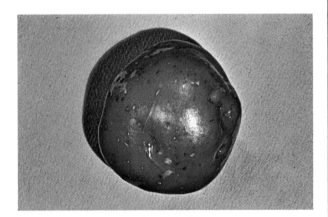

RED LaSODA

IRISH COBBLER

Potatoes of any kind or size should be firm, relatively smooth, clean, reasonably well shaped. They should not be badly cut or bruised or wilted, sprouted, sunburned or light-burned. Size does not affect quality and is a matter of choice for the particular use.

Some red potato varieties, some areas of production, are artificially colored with a red dye and wax. The wax and color used are non-toxic and used to enhance the appearance and preserve the freshness. Federal Food and Drug regulations require the potatoes so treated be plainly marked on the package or at the display area. A number of years ago, as a result of imperfect color in some of the new varieties of red potatoes, color-waxing was employed by many areas of production to provide a uniformity of color and ready identification of the red potatoes. Because boiling of this type of potato, with the skin on, caused an objectionable residue in the pan, many states have established laws prohibiting sale of color-waxed potatoes.

Today, some areas also clear-wax their Russet and White varieties to enhance the appearance and preserve freshness. The objectionable pan residue has virtually been eliminated.

In the future, potatoes will probably be sold by not only grade and size, but also specific gravity. The latter test is your very best guide to cooking characteristics. The higher the specific gravity of the potato, the more mealy it usually is; thus, ideal for baking. A potato of slightly lower specific gravity is better for boiling, and one of still lower specific gravity is preferred for frying.

If a potato placed in a 1.08 salt solution sinks, its specific gravity is greater than 1.08. If it floats, it may be placed in a 1.07 solution and the test repeated. Rather ideal specific gravity for baking and mashing potatoes is considered 1.08. For boilers, between 1.07 and 1.08; for fryers, below 1.07.

If you just *have to know* the cooking characteristics of your potatoes in the home, make a solution of 22 oz. of common salt in 11 pints of water. Potatoes of specific gravity of 1.08 or higher will sink in such a solution.

For years, "Blue Goose" has been the largest factor in marketing potatoes from leading producing states. The brand represents "the best of the better crops".

HELPFUL TIPS ON POTATOES

Baking: Insert an aluminum or stainless steel kitchen nail into each potato before placing in oven. This will promote uniform baking throughout the tubers.

Don't ever attempt to bake a full-skin, mature potato without puncturing the skin — they might "explode"!

Peeling: It is best to boil potatoes in their skin — helps preserve the nutritive values. After boiling, skins will slip off easily after a sharp, initial slice to puncture the skin; saves time, too.

Boiling: Do so with skin on — in minimum amount of water and only until just done to desired degree of softness. Pour off water, turn down flame, place vessel back on fire until the sizzle stops. Then, most of the water absorbed by the potatoes will be dissipated. Now peel, mash, etc.

Stews: Never peel and cut potatoes to cook *in* with the stew, for the potatoes will become tired, soggy and lose their character. Boil the potatoes *separately*, peel and add to the plate of stew.

Salty soup: Cut a raw potato in half and put it in a small kettle of soup that is too salty. Boil for a short time until the over-saltiness disappears, then remove the potato.

Mashing more lightly: Hot milk is better than cold milk for adding to potatoes to be mashed. A teaspoonful of baking powder added before mashing will make them light and creamy, too . . . especially if they're whipped briskly.

Browning fried potatoes: Sprinkle the sliced potatoes to be fried with a pinch of flour to make them a golden brown color.

Odor removal: Onion odor can be removed from a knife by running through a potato several times.

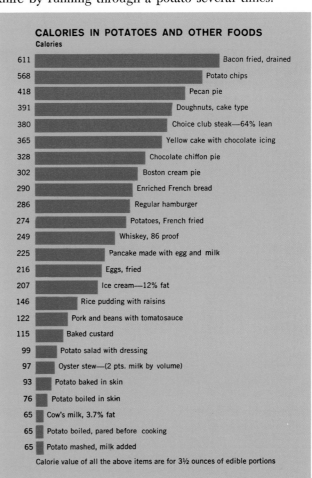

CALORIES IN POTATOES AND OTHER FOODS

Calories

Calories	Food
611	Bacon fried, drained
568	Potato chips
418	Pecan pie
391	Doughnuts, cake type
380	Choice club steak—64% lean
365	Yellow cake with chocolate icing
328	Chocolate chiffon pie
302	Boston cream pie
290	Enriched French bread
286	Regular hamburger
274	Potatoes, French fried
249	Whiskey, 86 proof
225	Pancake made with egg and milk
216	Eggs, fried
207	Ice cream—12% fat
146	Rice pudding with raisins
122	Pork and beans with tomato sauce
115	Baked custard
99	Potato salad with dressing
97	Oyster stew—(2 pts. milk by volume)
93	Potato baked in skin
76	Potato boiled in skin
65	Cow's milk, 3.7% fat
65	Potato boiled, pared before cooking
65	Potato mashed, milk added

Calorie value of all the above items are for 3½ ounces of edible portions

DISTRIBUTION OF U.S. POTATO PRODUCTION by STATE AND HARVEST SEASON

(000 Hundredweight)

	Winter	Early Spring	Late Spring	Early Summer	Late Summer	Fall	Total
ALABAMA			1,120	1,170			2,290
ALASKA							—1
ARIZONA			2,944				2,944
ARKANSAS			126				126
CALIFORNIA	1,848		14,606	1,980	2,618	7,924	28,976
COLORADO					2,948	8,695	11,643
CONNECTICUT						1,215	1,215
DELAWARE				1,680			1,680
FLORIDA	1,980	5,284					7,264
GEORGIA			165	130			295
HAWAII							—1
IDAHO						67,000	67,000
ILLINOIS					456		456
INDIANA					171	1,396	1,567
IOWA					462		462
KANSAS				108			108
KENTUCKY				197			197
LOUISIANA			225				225
MAINE						35,100	35,100
MARYLAND				288	98		386
MASSACHUSETTS						950	950
MICHIGAN					2,052	6,744	8,796
MINNESOTA					1,975	13,500	15,475
MISSISSIPPI			200				200
MISSOURI				110			110
MONTANA						1,388	1,388
NEBRASKA					352	1,794	2,146
NEVADA						297	297
NEW HAMPSHIRE						176	176
NEW JERSEY					3,250		3,250
NEW MEXICO					478		478
NEW YORK, L. I.					1,820	6,812	8,632
NEW YORK, UPSTATE						8,342	8,342
NORTH CAROLINA			1,569	230	145		1,944
NORTH DAKOTA						15,400	15,400
OHIO					640	1,925	2,565
OKLAHOMA			302				302
OREGON						13,115	13,115
PENNSYLVANIA						7,810	7,810
RHODE ISLAND						1,326	1,326
SOUTH CAROLINA			860				860
SOUTH DAKOTA						561	561
TENNESSEE				353			353
TEXAS	403		500	3,534			4,437
UTAH						1,332	1,332
VERMONT						254	254
VIRGINIA				3,837	81		3,918
WASHINGTON					7,866	21,420	29,286
WEST VIRGINIA					368		368
WISCONSIN					3,520	8,880	12,400
WYOMING						578	578
TOTAL	3,828	5,687	22,617	13,617	29,300	233,934	308,984

The seasonal classification of potatoes is based on the time when **most** of the crop is **usually** harvested, as follows: **Winter** is January, February, March; **Early Spring** is April 1 to May 15; **Late Spring** is May 16 to June 30; **Early Summer** is July 1 to August 15; **Late Summer** is August 16 to September 30 and **Fall** is October, November, December. (Above figures based 1969 crop year.)

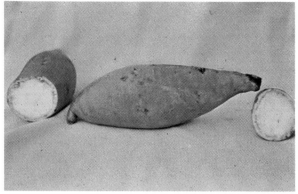

PORTO RICAN

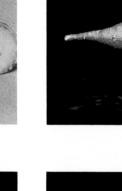

RED VELVET

UNWASHED YAMS

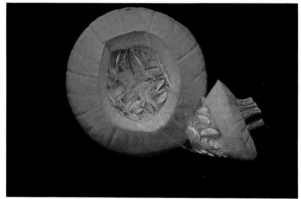

PUMPKIN

SWEET POTATOES

The sweet potato is a native American plant, found by Columbus and mentioned in the records of his fourth voyage. It is believed that they also found sweet potatoes on earlier voyages to the West Indies.

The kind of sweet potato to select is really a matter of your own personal taste. Sweet potatoes are of two types — the *dry-meated* and the *moist-meated*. The "moist" type is often called "yam"; however, the true yam is of a different genus.

The skin of the dry type is usually light yellowish-tan or fawn-colored, while the skin of the moist-fleshed varieties vary in color from whitish-tan to brownish-red.

Disregard color in sweet potato buying, but remember that thick, chunky, medium-size sweets, which taper toward the ends, are preferable. Avoid those with any sign of decay, as such deterioration spreads rapidly, affecting the taste of the entire potato. Buy bright, clean sweets that are free from blemishes. You can enjoy them the year around.

Centennial, Nemagold, Goldrush, Georgia Red, Porto Rico, Jersey and Velvets are the top seven ranking varieties of production.

Centennial: soft-flesh type, roots tapered to cylindrical, medium to large, orange skin and deep-orange flesh.

Nemagold: flesh fairly soft when baked. Roots medium size, short to long spindle, with russet-golden-orange skin and deep-orange flesh. Skin usually smooth, but sometimes veined.

Goldrush: excellent quality for market and canning. Soft-flesh type. Roots tapered; spindle uniform, attractive bright orange skin and deep-orange flesh. Smooth skin.

Georgia Red: soft-flesh type. Roots slightly variable. Purplish-red to copper-red skin and orange flesh. Excellent for baking.

Porto Rico: light rose to rose skin color with orange-yellow flesh. Shape of root is fusiform to globular and irregular, but smooth.

The Sweet Potato is one of the most complete foods known. The natives of the highlands of western New Guinea are reported to subsist almost entirely on sweet potatoes. One medium (5 x 2″) boiled, peeled sweet potato provides more than twice the recommended daily allowance of Vitamin A for an adult, 36% of the Vitamin C and a good amount of other vitamins and minerals. Magnesium content of raw sweet potatoes, 100 grams

(3½ oz.) of edible portion, is about 31 milligrams, the same amount of raw sweet potato contains approximately 114 calories; baked in skin, 141 calories; boiled in skin 114 calories.

For short periods of storage, approximately 55° F., low humidity, is best.

Sweet potatoes are among the most easily prepared of all vegetables. They may be boiled, baked, browned, fried and candied. They can be used to make biscuits, bread, muffins, pies, custards, cookies or cakes. Remember, however, that to give their best nutriment and flavor, sweet potatoes should be cooked in the jackets, which slip off easily and promptly at a slight pressure of finger or knife.

"Sweets" are available every month of the year, heaviest from September through March. Louisiana, New Jersey, California and North Carolina, in that order, are the leading producing states.

PUMPKIN

The common field pumpkin can be traced back traditionally to the early settlers. It is a member of the same family as muskmelons and squash and is usually classed as a vegetable.

The states having the greatest acreage in pumpkins, whether for fresh market or processing, are Illinois, California, New Jersey, with Illinois having more than twice the acreage of the second state. About 80% of the pumpkins marketed fresh are from domestic sources.

Besides the common use of pumpkins for Halloween, pumpkins provide the makings of spicy pumpkin pie, bread or muffins; various puddings and custards; as well as stuffing with meats and vegetables or meats and seafood in the smaller ones.

Size and shape have little to do with a pumpkin's flavor, although the smaller ones have less waste and usually a more tender flesh.

Pumpkins are an excellent source of Vitamin A, and 100 grams of edible portion (canned) pumpkin contains only 33 calories; raw, 26 calories. Magnesium content of pumpkins is 12 milligrams per 100 grams of edible portion.

RADISHES

China is believed to be the country of origin of this vegetable.

Good quality in fresh radishes is not indicated by the condition or color of the leaves, but by the root, which should be smooth, crisp and firm, never soft or spongy. The long, white, mild-flavored ones are called "icicles"

but the small red "button" variety is more popular. Round radishes vary in size from about an inch in diameter up to four inches; the long ones from three inches up to ten inches in length. They are plentiful every month of the year!

In addition to the most popular varieties just mentioned, there is also a round white and a round black radish.

Because of the better keeping quality of radishes without tops, the most common method of selling radishes is in a plastic-type bag containing four, six or eight ounces of topped radishes. Best storage temperature is 32° F., with very high humidity. If storing bunched radishes, addition of ice helps keep tops fresh. Eat them raw or may also be cooked and eaten with a cream sauce. The consumers of many countries are very fond of radish tops.

Radishes provide only 17 calories per 100 grams of edible portion, a good portion of the daily recommended allowance of Vitamin C, as well as a good amount of potassium and magnesium, with a fair contribution of other minerals and vitamins. Eaten raw, radishes are one of the important detergent foods helpful to dental health.

RHUBARB

Botanically, rhubarb is a vegetable; however, in use, it is considered a fruit.

Fresh field or hothouse rhubarb is frequently referred to as "pieplant" and is available all year, with heaviest supplies January through August.

Field grown rhubarb is rich, dark red in color, with coarse, green foliage and a very tart flavor. It is sold with leaves attached or removed. Hothouse rhubarb is light pink with small leaves and is almost stringless. It has a milder flavor and tops are usually trimmed before selling.

Rhubarb of good quality is fresh, firm, crisp, tender and either cherry red or pink in color. The stalks should be fairly thick, with the younger stems on which the leaves are not fully grown usually the most tender and delicate in flavor. Stale rhubarb usually has a wilted, flabby appearance. Condition of the leaves is a reliable guide in judging freshness of this vegetable.

Fresh rhubarb stalks in good condition can be stored 2-4 weeks at 32° F., high relative humidity. Rhubarb wilts rapidly at room temperature.

A 3½ oz. serving of cooked rhubarb, with sugar added, provides 141 calories, while 100 grams of edible portion, raw, contains only 16 calories. Also provides a fair amount of Vitamins A and C, as well as potassium and magnesium.

RED BUNCH

WHITE RADISH

BLACK RADISH

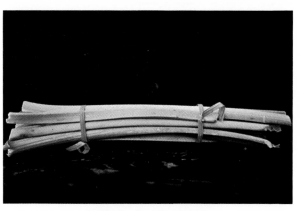

REGULAR RHUBARB

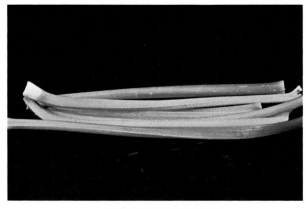

CHERRY RHUBARB

RUTABAGAS

SPINACH

Only the stalk of the rhubarb is suitable for consumption. The leaf, you will find, is very bitter, containing oxalic acid — if any quantity of leaves is eaten, it could be fatal.

Rhubarb stalks have long been popular in pies, tarts, sauces, puddings, punch, jams and jellies. They are easy to preserve and readily adaptable to freezing. May be baked or stewed and eaten as a breakfast food, side dish with other meals, or as a dessert. The cooked juice, with a sweetener added and chilled, makes a refreshing drink.

RUTABAGAS

Rutabagas, a popular vegetable with a good content of Vitamin A, are in season from July to April. The tops, which are not eaten, show first signs of deterioration and consequently, are usually trimmed off by retailers or their suppliers. The roots of good quality rutabagas should be smooth-skinned, firm and heavy for their size, although size is not a quality factor.

While there are white-fleshed and yellow-fleshed varieties, commercially rutabagas are virtually all yellow-fleshed.

Storage rutabagas are generally dipped in an edible vegetable wax to make them keep better, since the hot coating is effective in preventing wilting and loss of weight. It also improves the appearance (luster) slightly. Such a coated root is usually preferable. This comes off when the root is peeled, of course.

Rutabagas are round and slightly longish and have a more solid flesh than the turnip. They should be stored at 32° F., relative humidity of 95%. This is one of the few vegetables which has to be peeled before cooking.

Cook in large quantity of boiling, salted water, uncovered, until tender. Drain off the liquid, mash and season with desired herbs. May be served in fritters, puddings and pancakes, fried, glazed and in many casserole dishes.

Raw rutabagas (3½ oz. portion) contain approximately 46 calories; when cooked, about 35 calories. Rutabagas have much more Vitamin A than turnips, considerably more Vitamin C and more of other vitamins and minerals, but less iron. Rutabagas are low in sodium. Maine-grown rutabagas have been found to be a rich source of Vitamin C, a good source of potassium and magnesium.

Rutabagas are an excellent mixer and combine well with potatoes, carrots, apples and other fruits and vegetables to provide an unusual variety in the daily menu.

Considered a "cool-climate" crop, practically all rutabagas consumed in the U.S. are grown in Canada.

SPINACH

Present day boys and girls aren't the only ones who have had to eat spinach, as historical records show it was cultivated by the Greeks and Romans even before the Christian era, with probable origin in Iran. Today, spinach is one of our most commonly used vegetables. It is the most important crop grown for greens in the United States, with 17 states producing spinach commercially for the fresh market. According to a survey made in retail stores, spinach is one of the most popular greens with the consumer. In sales, it ranks about 14 among vegetables.

Well-developed plants with fresh, crisp, clean leaves of good green color are the best quality. Small, straggly or overgrown stalky plants are often tough. Those that are wilted or have started to turn yellow usually show sliminess and rot.

Both the crinkly-leaf and flat-leaf types are good for cooking. Incidentally, you won't have to wash spinach as much as usual if a little salt is dissolved in the first water you use.

You'll find spinach on the market all year, with major shipments coming from Texas. Its principal varieties are Broad Flanders and New Zealand.

Ideal storage temperature is 32° F., relative humidity 95-98%. Crushed ice in packages helps keep greens fresh. One pound of New Zealand spinach, raw, as purchased, contains only 86 calories, is an excellent source of Vitamins A and C, as well as potassium and magnesium. Also provides a wealth of natural food values in other vitamins and minerals.

The trick in serving good spinach is very quick cooking in a slight amount of water — only the amount that clings to the leaves after washing. Suggestions for serving include plain with melted butter and seasoned to taste; with hardboiled, chopped eggs; escalloped, molded or creamed; fondue, souffle or served with cheese; with bacon, vinegar and sugar. Very young, tender leaves may be used raw in salads. When eaten raw, spinach is considered a detergent food, helpful to dental health.

SQUASH

The term "summer" and "winter" for squash are only based on current usage, not on actuality. "Summer" types are on the market all winter; and "winter" types are on the market in the late summer and fall as well as winter, and some are on the market all year. Thus, the terms "summer" and "winter" are deceptive and confusing. Squash is produced commercially in 48

ACORN

BANANA

BUTTERNUT

HUBBARD

ITALIAN

SUMMER

YELLOW CROOK NECK

BUTTON, WHITE

states with Florida the leading producing state.

The soft-shell, immature squashes, such as *Yellow Crookneck* and *Zucchini*, should be obviously fresh, fairly heavy for size and of characteristic color. Rind should be so tender it is easily punctured with the fingernail. Seeds should be soft and fully edible. The soft-shelled, immature squash is 97% edible. *Cocozelle* is an example of this type of squash. It is widely grown and on the market all year. There are two general types: Long and Short, differing mainly in size.

Hard-shelled mature squashes are not expected to be fresh in the same sense as immature squash. The shell should be intact and show no decay. In this type of squash, the seeds are expected to be hard and inedible and are scooped out before or after cooking. Avoid squash that shows any soft or watery areas. These varieties are adapted for long storage. *Hubbards* can be successfully stored for six months or longer; *Table Queen (Acorn)* can be kept three to six months.

The popular varieties of squash in the soft-shelled, immature category include:

Yellow-Crookneck, one of the most widely grown. It is available all year, though not storage. Curved at the neck and larger at the apex than at the base; moderately warted, skin light yellow at early edible stage, turning to deeper color in mature stage; flesh creamy yellow. *Yellow Straightneck* is similar to Crookneck, but relatively straight. *Zucchini* is also widely grown and on the market all year. They are cylindrical, straight in shape; skin color moderately dark green over a ground color of pale yellow. Sometimes sold as "Italian" squash. *Cocozelle* is a bush squash with fruit almost cylindrical when young, with very slightly enlarged apex. Skin is smooth but ribbed widely and shallowly. Skin alternately striped in rather definite lines with very dark green or dull greenish black or pale greenish-yellow coloring. *Scallops* (pattypans) are widely grown and on the market all year. They are disk or flared — bowl shape with prominent ribbing on edge, giving escalloped appearance. Size is generally 3-4″ across. In the white type, they are pale green when young, becoming white later. Skin is smooth or slightly warted, flesh green tinged.

The hard-shelled, mature, varieties include *Acorn (Table Queen)*, which is widely grown and available all year. This squash is acorn-shaped, hence the name. *Buttercup* falls into this category and is so named because of the turban-like cap at the blossom end; shape somewhat drumlike, with sides slightly tapering near the apex. *Butternut,* also, is of this category, available all year; nearly cylindrical but with a slightly bulbous base; skin light creamy brown or dark yellow; shell smooth and hard; flesh yellow or orange and fine grained. *Large Banana* is on the market August through March. Fruit is nearly cylindrical and moderately tapering at base and apex; skin moderately smooth to obscurely wrinkled and pock-marked; color pale olive gray changing to creamy pink in storage.

Both the immature and mature squash are low in calories. The mature squash contributes far more Vitamin A than the soft-shell, soft-seeded squash; but, contributes less Vitamin C. Both are low in sodium, high in potassium, fair amount of magnesium.

For hard shell squash, ideal temperature for storage is 50° F., relative humidity 70-75%. For soft-shelled, immature squash, best temperature is 32-40° F., relative humidity 85-90%.

Summer squashes may be prepared in any of the usual ways for boiling and baking vegetables and may also be fried. Winter types are cut in halves or pieces, seeds are removed and the squash is then baked, steamed or boiled. Where water is used in cooking, the quantity of water should be kept small to avoid taking flavor and nutrients. Acorn and Butternut are frequently cut in half and baked and served in the shell. Squash pulp is also used for pie and may be served in casseroles, souffles, pancakes and custards.

TOMATOES

It seems likely the tomato is native to the Peru-Bolivia-Ecuador area of the Andes Mountains. For many centuries it has been one of the fundamentals in the Mexican diet. Until about 1834, the tomato was almost wholly unknown in this country as an esculent vegetable. Extensive commercial tomato production in the U.S. is not much over 90 years old. It may surprise you to learn that tomatoes, once known as "love apples", are actually a fruit, not a vegetable. Among fruits, it is a berry, being pulpy and containing one or more seeds that are not stones. It is also one of the few fruits and vegetables that gains weight as it matures.

There are probably four basic factors on which the consumer should evaluate the quality of tomatoes: color or general appearance, firmness and weight of the fruit (in relation to size), internal appearance of the sliced fruit, and flavor. A tomato can be of good quality whether large or small; size is a matter of preference. The ideal tomato, from the consumer's viewpoint, is one that is full size, vine ripened, unblemished and characteristically tomato-red.

With the exception of greenhouse-grown tomatoes, it is not practical to harvest tomatoes commercially at the red-ripe stage. Such fruit is too tender even to

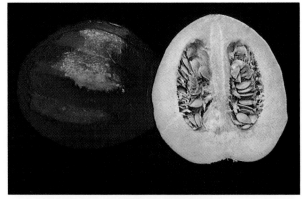

TABLE QUEEN

CHERRY

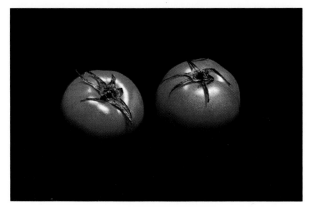

HOT HOUSE

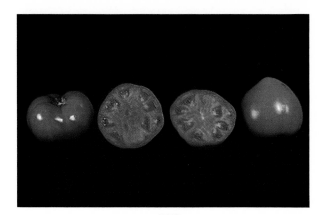

RED

stand harvesting, let alone packing and shipping; therefore, "vine-ripe" tomatoes are not fully vine ripe, but were harvested at the "turning" or pink stage. One exception to this is greenhouse-grown tomatoes. These are historically shipped in sturdy, small eight-pound units to protect the tomato and distribution generally confined to comparatively small areas within 500 miles.

Many tomatoes shipped to distant markets are harvested at the "mature-green" stage. At this stage, the fruits are about full grown, have heightened gloss because of the waxy skin that cannot be torn by scraping, internally have well-formed jelly-like substance and show no red color, but may show cream-colored streaks at the blossom end. Tomatoes, with stems attached, lose moisture more slowly and will keep fresh for a longer time than those with stems removed.

Tomatoes which are ridged and peaked at the stem end contain dry tissue and usually contain open spaces below the level of the stem scar and are not considered well developed.

Tomatoes are grown in all states for the fresh market, but Florida is the leading producer, with California a close second. The tomato is the leading greenhouse vegetable in the U.S., and it is also our leading fresh

import from Mexico during the winter and spring months.

Tomatoes are the principal crop grown hydroponically throughout the world, this method detailed elsewhere in this book.

Cherry Tomatoes: relatively minor crop in California, but are a comparatively high value crop. Red Cherry, Large, is probably the most popular variety. Plants are usually trained for erect growth by the use of stakes and horizontal strings. May grow as large as 2" in diameter, but generally 1-1½" — may or may not have some of the green calyx attached.

The best ripening temperatures for mature-green tomatoes are 65-70° F., with relative humidity of 85-88%. Tomatoes that are not fully ripened will ripen satisfactorily in a home if placed in an area with good air circulation, normal temperature and humidity, and *should not be refrigerated until such time as they are fully ripened.* After ripening, they can be held at 50° F. or lower.

A fresh, ripe tomato is very rich in Vitamins A and C, potassium, phosphorus and an all-around supply of other vitamins as well as important minerals. One medium size contains only 30 calories!

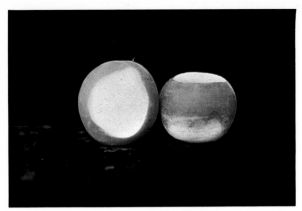

PURPLE TOP TURNIPS

CELANTRO (Coriander)

Small sizes are good for sauces and casseroles. Medium or large sizes are preferred for slicing. Jumbo sizes for stuffing or when served alone with desired dressing.

Fresh tomatoes are an ideal salad vegetable, served sliced or cut, in wedges, either alone or in combination with lettuce, asparagus, celery, cucumbers, onions and greens. It is a standard item in sandwiches, delectable in soup and the base for many delightful sauces and dressings. It can be a fine snack eaten out of hand, ice cold and salted. They are served cooked in many forms: stewed, fried, baked and in conserves. Large green tomatoes are often used for frying while small green ones are excellent for pickling.

When eaten raw, tomatoes are considered a detergent food, important to dental health.

TURNIPS

Turnips originated in Southern Europe where, during the earliest times, they were cultivated for medicinal purposes as well as for food. In fact, it was then popularly believed that broth made from turnips was good for the gout and that the turnip could be made into an excellent scouring soap for beautifying the face and hands. Whether there is any factual basis for such beliefs is problematical, but modern research has proven that turnips are a good source of several vitamins, the fresh green tops being particularly rich in A and C, with a high concentration of magnesium and calcium.

Canada is, by far, the largest single supplier.

The most popular variety of turnip is Purple Top White Globe. The root is large, globe-shaped, smooth, with irregularly marked purple cap; flesh is white, sweet, crisp and tender and the leaves are dark green, large and erect. There are some varieties which are grown almost exclusively for the leaves.

Turnips are generally sold with the tops removed, although those from early crops are sometimes sold in bunches with tops on. The eating quality of turnip greens depends largely on their freshness when purchased. Turnip greens are not suitable for storage for more than a week or two after being cut, and vary considerably in appearance, depending upon the variety and the stage of development at which they are harvested, 100 gr. edible portion contain only 28 calories.

One pound of raw turnips, without tops, has 88 calories and much the same nutrient characteristics of rutabagas. They may be served boiled with drawn butter and cream sauce; or boiled and mashed; or cut or sliced and cooked in stews or with roasts. Browned bacon adds to the flavor — and don't forget raw turnips in salads. Raw turnip is one of the important detergent vegetables helpful to dental health.

It is interesting to note that by adding a teaspoonful of sugar to the cooking water, turnips can be made sweeter and their flavor improved. Best storage temperature is 32° F., relative humidity 95-98%. White turnips are especially good in soups and stews. Yellow turnips are most often mashed.

WATERCRESS

Believed to be native to Asia Minor and the Mediterranean area, water cress is a perennial aquatic plant, generally cultivated in large ponds; it has long stems and small, thick leaves, having pungent flavor, and is most easily produced in water from springs in limestone regions. The best product comes from clear, running water or about springs where it can be watered frequently.

There is only one variety of the plant we call water cress; however, there are other cresses that grow wild and under similar conditions. Two field or land cresses that are seen on the market are peppergrass (sometimes called Fine Curled or Curled), which is a hardy, quick-

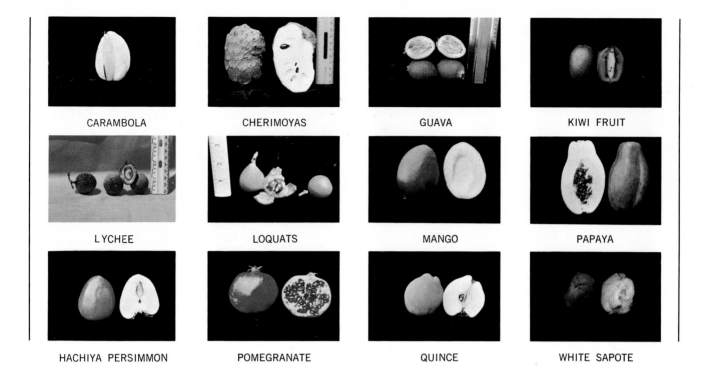

CARAMBOLA	CHERIMOYAS	GUAVA	KIWI FRUIT
LYCHEE	LOQUATS	MANGO	PAPAYA
HACHIYA PERSIMMON	POMEGRANATE	QUINCE	WHITE SAPOTE

growing annual having finely curled, deep green foliage, with pleasing flavor; and Upland cress, dwarf plant with slender stalks and oval notched leaves rather like water cress in shape and flavor. There are many other cresses, generally growing wild, mainly gathered in the spring and used as greens or as a substitute for water cress.

Water cress should be selected with an eye to its fresh bright green color and crispness of its rather long stems. Presence of wilted, bruised or yellowing leaves is a sign of age or poor handling.

As for other leafy greens, favorable storage temperature is 32° F., high humidity. Water cress can be kept in the home refrigerator for a week or more when proper care is taken in storage. It should not be placed in a refrigerator storage pan where it will be mashed by heavier vegetables or fruits. It should be washed gently, but thoroughly, in cold water, drained well and dried on a towel or absorbent paper. Place in a quart jar or other glass container with tight-fitting cover and store in coldest part of refrigerator, without freezing, and use when needed.

These greens are an excellent source of the ever-needed Vitamin C, calcium, phosphorus, potassium, magnesium, and Vitamin A, as well as a good portion of other vitamins and minerals, while providing only 19 calories per 100 grams edible portion — a further reason for including it in any salad.

The tangy leaves and tender stems of water cress are eaten raw in salads, combined with other tender greens, or as a garnish on hot and cold dishes. It lends an interesting flavor to soups and may be braised or cooked with other vegetables or added to sauces. The water cress sandwich is as English as apple pie is American; the French have popularized a thick soup made of potatoes and water cress; the Italians add it to their minestrone soups and the Chinese have long used it in their won ton and other soups. Hotels and restaurants are big users of water cress.

Raw greens, all kinds, are important detergent foods helpful to dental health.

"VARIETY" FRUITS, VEGETABLES

FRUITS

BREADFRUIT. Member of the mulberry family and widely dispersed in the torrid zones, breadfruit is a staple fruit of Polynesia. The plant was brought to the West Indies in 1792 by Captain Bligh on his second voyage and is grown in South and Central America as well as Mexico. Oval or round in shape and may grow up to watermelon size; 5-9″ long, 4-8″ in diameter and weigh 2-15 lbs. or more. Rind is yellowish-green, pulp is fibrous and white to yellowish when mature. The cultivated breadfruit is seedless and the wild breadfruit has seeds. The seed-bearing form is usually called breadnut and may be raised from seeds. This is grown for the seeds, primarily, which are roasted or boiled.

In the South Sea Islands, breadfruit is regarded as the "staff of life", one of their principal sources of native food. It is cooked like potatoes for eating. Compared to potatoes, raw breadfruit has 103 calories per 100 grams, potatoes 76; protein 1.7 grams in breadfruit, and 2.1 grams in potatoes.

CARAMBOLA *(care-am-bowl-a)*. Varies in size from a hen's egg to a large orange; may be ovate, acutely five-angled fruit. The Golden Star fruit is ovoid or ellipsoid in shape, from 4-5″ in length, with 4-6 prominent, longitudinal ribs. The skin is bright golden-yellow in color and has a thick, waxy cuticle. The flesh is juicy and crisp in texture and contains no fiber. Grown sparingly in Southern California and Florida, as well as West Indies, Hawaii. Many consider different varieties resulting in "sweet" types and "sour" types; however, fruits from seedlings produce the unpleasantly sour product and those from vegetatively propagated plants produce the superior fruit desired. The attractive appearance and exotic nature of the carambola make it attractive for gift packages, esteemed in fruit and vegetable salads. It is used in beverages, jellies and jams. It continues to grow in popularity in South Florida as a dooryard tree, but its super-sensitivity to cold weather and water have deterred large commercial growings. Fully ripe fruits have an agreeable flavor, mildly sub-acid to sweet, are a good source of carbohydrates and Vitamins A and C.

CHERIMOYA *(chair-i-moy-a)*. The cherimoya is almost heart-shaped, green-colored when ripe, with the skin marked faintly in medallions. It is grown in Southern Florida, Indies, Australia, California, is sometimes called *Custard Apple* and also "sherbet fruit" because of its natural sherbet texture when chilled. Flavor resembles a combination of fresh pineapple, strawberry and banana.

Choose ones with fairly uniform green color. The larger fruit is usually the best. Surface brown scars do not indicate poor quality, but avoid cherimoya with mold or cracks at the stem end, or those with dark brown skins, as they are probably over-ripe. Ripen at room temperature until they yield to gentle pressure from the palms of the hands.

It is cut in halves or quarters to eat with a spoon. The many seeds are removed as it is eaten. Cooks with a great deal of patience remove the seeds and use cherimoyas in fruit cups or salads. One (3½ oz.) medium fruit contains 94 calories.

CRABAPPLES. Mostly used in the making of jellies, jams and preserves. They're small in size (about 1½″ in diameter), with a sour taste that makes them unsuitable for eating out of hand. Choose them in the same manner as you would regular varieties of apples. Approximately 68 calories per 100 grams, 81.1% water.

GRANADILLA *(gran-a-dill-a)*. Passion Fruit: This fruit, sometimes called the purple granadilla, grows extensively in South America and Australia and is now being cultivated in California in increasing quantities. Passion fruit, which is the size and shape of an egg, has a tough, purple skin. The meat is yellow, with many black seeds and is generally eaten in the fresh stage with a spoon; also used in cakes, jellies or made into a beverage.

The passion fruit is said to derive its name from the fact that early Christian missionaries to South America, noticing it for the first time, saw in its flower formation symbols of the Crucifixion, the crown of thorns, nails, etc.

Sweet Granadilla: Not as well-known as the purple granadilla, though flavor considered even finer. Oval shaped, 3-6″ long, skin orange-brown, tough, leathery. Pulp is translucent and whitish. Uses are the same as passion fruit.

Granadilla, Giant: The largest of the granadillas, fruit oblong and measuring up to 10 inches in length. Resembles a short, thick vegetable marrow, yellow-green in color and contains a mass of purple sweet-acid pulp mixed with flat seeds. Flavor inferior to purple and sweet granadillas. In the West Indies, called "watermelon."

One hundred grams of edible portion of purple granadilla contains 90 calories and is high in potassium and Vitamin A, as well as a good amount of phosphorus and some calcium and Vitamin C.

GUAVA *(Gwa'-va)*. Grown extensively in Hawaii, Florida and Southern California, but native to Mexico and South America, this fruit is a member of the custard apple family, grown on small trees or bushes.

Fruit varies in size, shape, color and flavor. Most common varieties are pineapple and strawberry, so-called because of their similarity in flavor to these fruits. Shape is round, 1-4″ in length, usually with flesh ranging from white to deep pink or salmon red; numerous small seeds embedded in flesh toward the center of the fruit. Skin color from green to yellow, depending on variety.

For cooking, choose guavas that are firm to the touch; for eating out-of-hand, ripen at room temperature until they give slightly to gentle pressure. They may be refrigerated after reaching the ripe stage and will keep for some time.

Pineapple guavas are very rich in Vitamin C and A. They are widely used in jellies and preserves and guava cheese. The high Vitamin C content is not impaired by cooking; 100 grams (3½ oz.) edible portion contain 62-65 calories, depending on variety.

KIWI FRUIT *(kee-wee)*. Native of China, the fruit was first introduced into New Zealand in 1906 and has been commercially cultivated only in that country. In truth, the name of the fruit is a figment of the imagination of merchandisers from New Zealand, who visited Los Angeles wholesale and retail markets and decided there was a potential for several New Zealand-grown fruits. Since the fruit is really a Chinese gooseberry, and the name rather unenchanting, they decided to rename the fruit "Kiwi".

"Kiwi Fruit" appropriately not only identifies New Zealand, but also describes the appearance of a New Zealand native, the tiny Kiwi bird.

The fruit is light brown, "furry" appearing, measuring 2½-3½" in length. Elongated with a very tender, soft skin. The interior texture is very similar to the American gooseberry and quite delectable.

It should be soft as a ripe pear for best eating. Ripen at room temperature and then refrigerate. It can be eaten out-of-hand after peeling, incorporated into salads or fruit compotes. In the market from June to March.

Kiwi Fruit is a rich source of Vitamin C and has the curious property of tenderizing meat — sliced Kiwi Fruit rubbed over an inexpensive cut of steak will, in a few minutes, have tenderized the meat sufficiently for grilling purposes.

KUMQUATS *(come-kwatt)*. Native of China, kumquats are produced in the United States, China, Japan, South Africa, Australia, France. They resemble an orange, but the size is generally 2-2½", football-shaped. This fruit is unusual in that the skin is sweet and the flesh is tart. Used for Christmas table decorations, preserves, jellies, candied fruit. May be eaten raw, skin and all. Choose firm kumquats; they will keep for some time without refrigeration. High in potassium, calcium and Vitamins A and C, 100 grams of raw edible portion contain 65 calories.

LADY APPLES. This is one of the most exotic and unusual looking apples in the world of fruits. It is unsurpassed for decorative uses and has a unique and delightful flavor. Hardly one in a thousand Lady Apples qualify as Pomme d'Apie Glacee.

The latter is almost transparent in appearance, which lends itself to a different type of decorative effect if placed so that light shines through it. The apple has an unusual grape-like flavor. About the size of an apricot.

Lady Apples date back some 500 years, when monks in the south of France made champagne from them after finding that their juice responded more like the grape than any other apple. Some of the rare Pomme d'Apie Glacee were brought to Francis I, King of France, and he and his court were so enamored over them that for years all the available meager supplies were reserved for him.

The fruit is grown by a few orchardists in the U.S., one of the largest being in Missouri, and yet this Lady Apple orchard is not considered large in the commercial sense. A few hundred trees in Washington and perhaps this many scattered throughout Ohio and the Appalachian states.

LITCHI or LYCHEE *(lee-chee* or *lye-chee)*. Methods of spelling this fruit are as numerous as Chinese dialects! A schizophrenic fruit which can become a nut if it is dried after maturing. Vastly popular in Asia for 2,000 years, now grown in Jamaica, Hawaii, Brazil, Florida and California. The matured fruit looks like overgrown strawberries prior to being picked. After picking, the attractive-red color disappears. Fruit can be stored for two or three weeks without losing its flavor, which is similar to a Muscat grape — some say tastes more like raisins, or Royal Ann cherries.

The outer covering is hard and bitter, rough on the surface and divided into small scale-like areas from which short conical protuberances usually arise. In flavor it is sub-acid, strangely suggestive of a Royal Anne cherry, especially when cooked.

As a dried fruit, it is well-known and is shipped to the U.S. and other countries, while considerable quantity is preserved in syrup and exported. Like most other fruits, however, it is considered most delicious when fresh.

Dried lychees, 100 grams, contain 277 calories and are high in potassium, phosphorus and calcium. Fresh lychees, 100 grams, contain 64 calories.

LOQUAT *(lo-kwatt)*. Produced in Northern India, Japan, rare in U.S.; popular in Mediterranean countries. Fruit is round or oval, 1-3" in length, pale yellow or orange, with somewhat downy surface and up to 10 large seeds. Thin skin, flesh firm and mealy, color from white to deep orange, juicy, of sub-acid flavor, somewhat reminiscent of a cherry. Loquats have a flavor that can be appreciated by Americans lacking in educated palates. Eaten fresh, stewed, made into pies and jelly or sauce.

Trees can be propagated by seed but budding and grafting procedures are more desirable in orchards which must produce fruit commercially. The trees thrive in low, sub-tropical areas, which are a few thousand feet above sea level. The fruit is highly susceptible to frost damage.

Available during April and May. Is reportedly a cross between the banana and pineapple. Fair source of Vitamin A and potassium, with 48 calories per 100 grams of edible portion.

MANGOS. The mango probably originated in the Himalayan region of India and in Burma and Malaya, and has been cultivated for at least 4,000 years.

Mangos may be varied in size, and shape, depending on variety and area in which they are grown. They are generally eaten raw, but green mangos are often used in many forms of sauces or preserves, as well as for pickling. Buy mangos that are firm and let ripen at room temperature until the fruit gives easily to slight pressure. Refrigerate until ready for use — mangos should not be cut until just before serving, in order to conserve the aroma.

Once fully ripened they should be stored at 50° F. and 85% relative humidity.

Mangos are on the market from January through late August from various shipping areas. One 3½ oz. edible portion contains 66 calories and is an excellent source of Vitamins A and C, as well as potassium, calcium and phosphorus.

MANGOSTEEN. Native to the Far East, this unusual fruit is similar in taste to the lychee and mango. May be eaten out-of-hand or made into preserves. Exterior is reddish-brown in color with a thick and very hard rind enclosing a number of segments (like those of an orange). The juicy flesh has a flavor described as suggesting those of the peach and pineapple. The pericarp of this fruit is used as an astringent. The size of a mandarin orange, round and slightly flattened at each end. White, juicy pulp with a sweet-tart flavor, cooling and refreshing. May contain five to seven segments and probably 1-3 of the segments contain seeds, which are very flavorful.

Nutritionally, 100 grams provide the following: 83.0% water; 63 calories; .6 gm. protein; 8 mg. calcium; 12 mg. phosphorus, .8 mg. iron; and 2 mg. Vitamin C.

PAPAYAS (pa-pie-ya). The papaya is native to tropical America but the original home is unknown. The plant grows almost like weeds throughout the tropics. They are extensively cultivated for export in Hawaii, while considerable amounts are grown in Puerto Rico and Florida. California grows some in the far south; however, the main source of supply for consumption is Hawaii.

Select fruit that is well colored, not green, but at least half yellow; should be smooth, unbruised, unbroken, showing no signs of deterioration or shriveling and be well shaped.

Papayas are available the year around, with peak production in the late winter and early spring.

The fruit is picked in the firm-ripe state and will ripen in 3-5 days at room temperature. After ripening, can be stored as low at 32° without damage. Fruit that is all yellow is generally ready to eat, and will keep for a week of two. The seeds are also edible: put in blender and blend only until they are cut to the size of coarsely ground pepper and add to salad dressing. Excellent source of Vitamins A and C, potassium and phosphorus, with 100 grams (3½ oz.) raw containing only 39 calories.

The milk-like juice of the papaya is prized as a remedy for dyspepsia because of its papain content, and in some Eastern cities, it is being bottled and marketed as a healthful soft drink.

PASSION FRUIT. See "Granadilla" elsewhere in this section.

PAPAWS (pawpaws). Native to North America, the papaw is the oblong, yellowish fruit of an annonaceous tree of Central and Southern United States. The fruit has a sweet banana-like, many-seeded pulp. Papaws are often confused with papayas but actually these two fruits are different. Papaws are about 6″ in length, width of about 3″ and an average weight of ¾ lb. Flesh is yellow, creamy in texture, and has a pungent odor. They are often *not* enjoyed at first — a taste for them having to be acquired. Contain mostly water, some protein and a trace of fat, little phosphorus and sodium; 8,500 I.U.'s of Vitamin A, 172 calories, with a trace of thiamine, riboflavin, niacin and ascorbic acid per 100 grams of edible portion.

PERSIMMONS. Known as the "apple of the orient", this rich, sweet fruit is an excellent addition to your fruit diet. Comes in two major varieties: *Hachiya*, which is slightly pointed in shape, bright orange color; and, the *Fuyu* (Fuji), same bright color but flatter in shape.

Hachiya is the leading variety in this country, accounts for 90% of the total, and is sweet when soft-ripe. Must be soft-ripe before they are eaten. The Fuyu variety is eaten out of hand like an apple, as well as being sliced. Buy soft ones for immediate use and firm ones to ripen at home and use as desired. Should be refrigerated as soon as they become soft.

Persimmons are available October to January, ripen best in a cool, dark place. They are relished for their luscious taste and contain only 77 calories per 100 grams edible portion, plus an excellent source of Vitamins A, C and potassium, phosphorus, calcium.

Persimmons can be eaten out-of-hand, or in a bowl with cream, and can be used in a number of different recipes such as persimmon pudding, cookies, cakes, for a delightful and unusual change in your menu.

There has been a widespread notion that persimmons are "astringent" in flavor, but this is largely a myth, generated by some persons attempting to eat the fruit *before* it has properly ripened. Unlike many fruits, persimmons attain full skin color *before they are ripe!* Persimmons are picked when mature, but must be shipped while hard, in order to ripen at the market or at the homemaker's kitchen.

Fruit may be ripened overnight by wrapping in foil and placing in the freezer compartment of your refrigerator. The next morning the fruit will be ready to eat, or put in a recipe, after thawing at room temperature for several hours until soft. But, the fruit must then be used immediately.

PLANTAIN. Greenish looking bananas, with quite rough skins and a number of blemishes. It is an important food in all tropical countries. While resembling the banana, they are long and thicker than bananas. Frequently used as a vegetable, rather than a fruit, and are usually found on the vegetable stand rather than in the fruit department. Even when fully ripe, fruit remains starchy and thus used primarily for baking, mashing, frying. Never eaten raw. Use as a substitute for baked potatoes — or they are excellent fried as a meat accompaniment. Do not refrigerate unless they become quite soft.

One 3½ oz. portion of plantain, raw, contains 119 calories, is an excellent source of potassium, good source of Vitamin C and fair amount of phosphorus.

PLUMCOTS. A cross between the plum and apricot, plumcots have a red flesh and a purple skin. Select them as you would apricots. Plumcots have very little acceptance in the market, as they are not very widely known or grown.

POMEGRANATES. The pomegranate is grown in many subtropical areas. In the U.S. it can be grown in the southern areas, but all commercial production is in California.

"Pomegranate" literally means "apple with many seeds". This is a colorful autumn fruit about the size of a large apple, hard-rinded and varying in color from yellow to deep red.

Good quality fruit will have unbroken rind, with no sign of decay; be heavy for its size and have a fresh, not dried-out appearance.

The *Wonderful* or *Red Wonderful* is the principal commercial variety. The fruit is large, glossy and of deep red or purple color. They are in season from September until the early part of December, with 60% of the supplies in October.

Large sizes are better as the kernels are juicier and better developed inside; but, regardless of the size of pomegranate, all pomegranates have approximately the same number of seeds. Each seed and its edible pulp is surrounded by a spongy-soft membrane, which is quite bitter. Only the seed is edible for fresh use.

Sprinkle a few pomegranate seeds into a salad — they make a bright jewel-like garnish and have an unusual flavor and texture. The seeds in their pulp capsules are easily removed when the fruit is cut in half and they can be held in the freezer indefinitely. When keeping the whole fruit for short periods of time, room temperature, out of sunlight, is ideal. Refrigeration will not hurt; could aid storage by adding moisture. Pomegranate juice is the base for grenadine syrup, so the fresh juice is very compatible to tropical drinks. Also can be frozen and used as desired.

The pulp (seed) is 82.3% water, contains 63 calories per 100 grams of edible portion, as well as small amounts of other vital nutrients, heavier to potassium.

PRICKLY PEARS. Prickly pears (Indian fig, barberry fig, and tuna) are the delicious fruit of a species of cactus and are most abundant during fall and early winter. They range in color from yellow to crimson and have spines which can be easily removed by singeing before the fruit is peeled. Heaviest supplies originate in Washington, Oregon.

Choose those that are firm but not hard, with a bright, fresh appearance, when shopping for this unusual fruit. Heaviest supply, September to December.

Prickly pears are red when ripe. Most in markets have been de-spined. Prickly pears are cut into pieces, or sliced, for eating.

Low in calories, have fair values of Vitamins A and C, potassium, and contain small amounts of other vital elements.

QUINCE. The quince is an autumn fruit which is generally grown for use in jelly-making and preserving. Good quality quinces are firm, free from blemishes and show a pale yellow color when fully ripe. They bruise very easily and must be handled carefully, although they may be kept for a very long period of time in a dry, cool place. May be round or pear-shaped, resembles an apple with a rather misshapen stem end. There is usually a rather woolly surface on the yellow skin. The flavor is more acid-bitter than an apple and has numerous hard seeds throughout.

Choose quince that are large and smooth, as the small knotty ones are wasteful. May be used for sauce, dessert or in puddings, pies and tarts. Excellent baked. Some of the oldtimers in the business tell us that if you place a quince in your closet or cupboard, it will keep the air fresh.

A 3½ oz. portion results in 57 calories, a good amount of Vitamin C, calcium, potassium and phosphorus.

SAPOTE (sa-po-tee, or tay). Also called the Mexican custard apple, it is one of the principal foods of that country. It is grown in many citrus areas in a small way. Clusters of the fruit are large, greenish-yellow. The White sapote is the most readily available on a commercial basis in the United States. It resembles a green apple in appearance but without an indentation on the blossom end.

Choose firm sapotes, free of bruises, with greenish to yellow-green color. Allow to ripen and soften at room temperature and then refrigerate. May be eaten fresh out-of-hand or made into a preserve or jam. Also referred to as marmalade plums.

There are four principal varieties: Sapote, Black Sapote, White Sapote and Yellow Sapote. Store as you would plums.

Fair amount of Vitamin A, small amount of Vitamin C and other nutritional elements.

STAR APPLE. In Cuba, Jamaica and several other tropical American countries, the star apple is a common dooryard tree and its fruit is held in much the same estimation as the sapote. The fruit is commonly round, 2-4″, the surface is smooth, somewhat dull purple in some varieties, light green in others. The fruit is usually eaten fresh, but in Jamaica is sometimes made into preserves. Must be left on tree until fully ripe or it is astringent. Cultivated to some extent in Mexico, Florida and South America, and a very little in Hawaii. The flesh is melting, sweet and pleasantly flavored.

TAMARIND. The fruit is a pod, cinnamon brown in color, 3-8″ long and flattened. Within its brittle covering are several obovate compressed seeds surrounded by brown pulp of acid taste, which are used in cooking and to prepare refreshing drinks. It is widely used in Oriental chutnies and curries; is also used, with the addition of sugar and water, to yield a cooling drink or "refresco", especially well-known in Latin America.

High in calories, tamarinds contain a good amount of calcium, phosphorus and potassium, with small amounts of protein, iron and Vitamin C.

UGLI FRUIT (ugly). A native to Jamaica, it has become popular because it is such a miserable-looking piece of fruit. About size of a grapefruit, extremely rough peel, badly disfigured, with light-green blemishes which turn orange when fruit is mature. Very juicy, large quantities of pulp and rather delightful orange-like flavor. Spherical to oblate appearance. Skin rather loose. Grown in Florida, also, in small quantities. Use and store as other citrus.

VEGETABLES

BAMBOO SHOOTS. Grown mostly in the Southern States, edible bamboo shoots are the tender young stalks of a species of bamboo plant. They resemble asparagus spears in appearance. Freshness, crispness and a good, green color are general indications of quality; 100 grams edible portion contain 27 calories and are a fair source of potassium.

BEAN SPROUTS. These crisp tendrils have been around for centuries, spending most of their culinary lives in Oriental dishes. Cooked or raw, bean sprouts have a fresh, delicate flavor and unusual shape and texture which add new dimension to vegetable combinations, salads and main dishes. Fresh looking, crisp, with tips that are not dry. The shorter the bean sprout, the younger and more tender it is.

Store in vegetable drawer in refrigerator. If you plan to serve them raw, wash well, float off the loose particles and chill in ice water for half an hour before serving.

It is easy to grow bean sprouts at home. Most commonly used is the mung bean, but any dried bean will do.

People generally mean "pea sprouts" when they say "bean sprouts". Pea sprouts are tiny shoots issuing from a little pea. When bought, the pea sprouts still carry an olive-green hood, which should be plucked off during the washing. If the roots at the tail of the snow-white stem are too long, they should also be plucked off. Bean Sprouts are usually golden yellow in color and possess a stronger flavor and a rather crunchy texture. The hood color varies according to the type of bean used. This hood must be removed.

Bean Threads are long, clear, dried "threads" made from mung beans, are most commonly used in Chinese soups. The Japanese use them in sukiyaki. They have a bland flavor and add a desirable chewy quality to a dish. Before using, you must soak the threads in water for several hours or overnight.

The nutritional values in sprouts from soybeans are more than in the same amount of mung bean sprouts; however, all varieties mentioned above have a high content of water, generally represent some volume of protein, vitamins and minerals — but not importantly so.

BEANS, Chinese Long (Dow Kwok). Chinese long beans are available the year around from California and Mexico. They are pencil-thin, light green and tender, about 12 inches long, usually, but may attain a length of 20-25 inches! Usually cooked with beef, the tiny bean within the pod resembles immature black-eyed peas. To our knowledge, the nutritive value is not

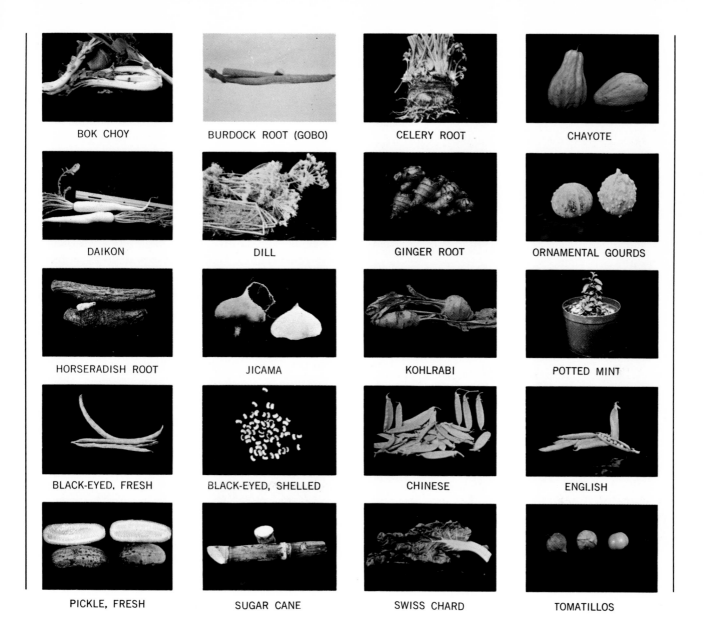

BOK CHOY   BURDOCK ROOT (GOBO)   CELERY ROOT   CHAYOTE

DAIKON   DILL   GINGER ROOT   ORNAMENTAL GOURDS

HORSERADISH ROOT   JICAMA   KOHLRABI   POTTED MINT

BLACK-EYED, FRESH   BLACK-EYED, SHELLED   CHINESE   ENGLISH

PICKLE, FRESH   SUGAR CANE   SWISS CHARD   TOMATILLOS

published on these beans. We assume the value would parallel green snap beans.

BITTER MELON. Balsam pear, commonly known as Bitter Melon; a clear, green vegetable, it is about the size of a cucumber and possesses a wrinkled surface. Inside is a layer of white or pink spongy pulp and seeds. Six to eight inches long, used for soup or fried with beef. Available from June to October.

BOK CHOY (Chinese Chard). Bok choy resembles both chard and celery. It is also called white mustard cabbage. It is a very leafy green vegetable with white stems and shiny dark leaves, often topped with a pale yellow flower. You can usually buy either the whole cluster, including tougher stalks, or just the heart or tender stem cluster, with the tough exterior stalks removed. Either is sold by the pound. Flavor is slightly stronger than that of Chinese cabbage, but it is good

cooked as a vegetable or in soups, and generally used in the preparation of Chinese chop suey and chow mein, etc. Leaves should be prepared as you would spinach.

Good quality contains 69 calories per lb. of food as purchased; high in calcium, Vitamin A, protein, Vitamin C and other elements.

BURDOCK (Gobo). Species of Arctium, from the Greek word for "bear", probably alluded to the shaggy "bur". Gobo is heavily cultivated in Japan for its root, which has been greatly thickened and ameliorated, affording a popular vegetable. The Burdock is a common and despised weed in this country, although it is capable of making an excellent foliage screen.

CACTUS LEAVES (Nopales). In April and May, cactus plants make new growth. The little leaves, or pencos, are light green and as crisp and tender as lettuce. Nopales are a favorite Mexican vegetable, with flavor and texture similar to green beans, but firmer. The smaller leaves are more tender.

To prepare for cooking, the cactus thorns must be removed, carefully, with a potato peeler or sharp-pointed knife. Cut the de-spined Nopales into half-inch squares and boil in salted water with ¼ tsp. of soda and one chopped onion for 20 small, tender Nopales. It should require 5-10 minutes to cook them tender. Drain, season to taste and serve.

CARDOON. A long celery-like vegetable, measuring nearly two feet, with a narrow, coarse top leaf. It is thought to be of the same species as the Globe artichoke and to have been developed from it by long cultivation and selection.

The plant has been introduced in South America and has grown wild extensively in the Pampas.

Leaves should be very dark green. Select cardoon with a small shank as this indicates a young, tender plant. Remove the outer stems as they only become tougher when cooked. The inner leaves and stalks have a pleasant flavor and can be substituted for celery. Store like celery. Vinegar added to the water (about 1 tsp. to a cup) will keep the cardoon white. The roots and leaf stalks are usually cooked and eaten in soups.

CELERIAC (se-ler'-i-ak). Also known as celery root, this vegetable is cultivated for its root instead of for its stalk. The leaves are not eaten after the manner of celery. Is grown the same as celery, for the thickened edible corm, except that no branching is required.

Choose celeriac that is small, since the smaller celeriac will be more tender and less woody. Trim roots and tops and store in refrigerator, 32° F., with high humidity.

It is a light brown bulb-type root. Best to peel before cooking. Primarily used in stews and soups, but can be braised or used as a substitute for cooked potatoes.

The raw celery knob may be peeled and cut into Julienne strips. Marinate the strips in French dressing for an hour and then drain, squeezing slightly to remove any excess liquid. Mix with mayonnaise and serve well-chilled on crisp lettuce leaves. The knob may be cooked in boiling, salted water and will be tender in ten minutes or so. A little vinegar or lemon juice added to the water will keep the celeriac white; 100 grams, raw, is equal to 40 calories.

CELTUCE (sell-tuss). A comparatively new vegetable in the U.S., celtuce has been grown in China for many years. This type has an enlarged stem and no head. The leaves are not palatable, as those of other types, except possibly while they are young and tender. It is grown principally for its large, fleshy stems which are peeled and eaten raw or cooked. Its flavor is a combination of celery and lettuce, from which it derives its name. Choose and store the same as you would lettuce.

CHARD. "Swiss Chard" is a type of beet that develops no enlarged, fleshy root. It has large leaves with thickened mid-ribs and both ribs and leaves are palatable. The roots are hard and woody. Like all salad greens, it is important the leaves be fresh, crisp and of a good, green color. It is an excellent source of Vitamin A and has a fair content of Vitamin C, potassium, phosphorus and calcium. High in magnesium; 100 grams edible portion, raw, is equal to 25 calories; 100 grams, cooked, boiled, drained, is equal to 18 calories. Ideal storage is at 34° F., at 90% humidity.

In effect, it is two vegetables in one, since the leaves may be cooked as greens and the white stems may be cooked like celery. The fiber is very delicate, similar to asparagus. It should always be steamed, never boiled. The leaves should be cooked like spinach, using only the water that clings to them after washing. Cream of Chard soup, made like cream of spinach, can be a delicious luncheon or supper dish.

CHAYOTE (chay-o-tee). (Vegetable pears). Grown successfully in California, Louisiana, Florida. Fruit is round to pear-shaped, smooth or corrugated, the surface sometimes is covered with small soft spines. Quality vegetable pears are quite fiberless, with little or no seed coat around the single flat seed. Deeply wrinkled, fibrous seed coat makes it unfit to eat. The darker green and the harder they are, the better. More delicately flavored than the squash. Grown on vines, a single vine may yield 50-100 fruits a season. Easily shipped and may be stored at room temperature for 2-4 months. It is a cousin to the cucumber and squash.

Creole cooks call it Mirliton, South Americans call it mango squash, Floridians call it the vegetable pear. Whatever name you use, it is one of the most versatile of all fresh vegetables, used in soups, salads, main dishes and in desserts.

Choose chayotes like a vegetable, not as a fruit. High in Vitamin C, 100 grams of edible portion, raw, provides some Vitamin A, and potassium, 28 calories.

CHERVIL (sher-vill). Member of the parsley family, salad chervil is a leafy vegetable used like parsley. Turnip-rooted chervil, sometimes called parsnip chervil, is served with its roots cooked like parsnips. It is grown as a spring or autumn crop, not thriving in the heat of summer. A native of Caucasus, Southern Russia and Western Asia.

Raw chervil provides approximately 57 calories per 100 grams of edible portion, plus a minor amount of ascorbic acid. It contains almost no other nutritional elements.

CORIANDER/CILANTRO. The Spanish name for coriander is cilantro, is native to Southern Europe and the Orient and has a very ancient history. The ripe seeds of coriander have served as a spice and a seasoning from very ancient times, the seeds having been found in Egyptian tombs. It is, or has been, cultivated in most of Europe and Asia; in the U.S., Kentucky produces more than other States. Sometimes called Chinese parsley or Mexican parsley.

Coriander is the dried ripe fruits of the plant. Cilantro is the parsley-like leaf of the coriander plant. Leaves are slightly more tender than parsley, but may be used in any way parsley is used. Flavor is zesty and lingers on the tongue. When substituting for parsley, you will need less cilantro.

Good green color and fresh, unwilted leaves mean good quality. Wash well and store in refrigerator drawer in plastic film bag.

DAIKON (die-con). Japanese radish. Large, long, tapered, 8-10 inches long, about 1¼-1½″ in diameter at the top. Has a flavor similar to ordinary radishes but a bit hotter. Pickled whole in large tubs with rice hulls added to the brine, it is served shredded as a relish, thinly sliced in soups or cut in thin strips on vegetable trays. Is an excellent keeper and should be stored like radishes in refrigerator. One pound of edible portion as purchased contains only 67 calories, high in calcium, phosphorus, potassium and Vitamin C.

In Hawaii, 4 million pounds of daikon were produced in 1962 and nearly one-third of the tonnage of vegetables grown in Japan is daikon — some indication of its importance.

DILL. Also known as dillweed, it is a plant with pungent, aromatic seeds which are dried and used mostly for pickling; a native of Southeastern Europe. They may also be utilized for flavoring soups and salads. Select dill the same as you would any fresh salad green.

GINGER ROOT. This is possibly one of the least glamorous appearing items in the produce department of your market, but it can elevate an ordinary fruit salad into something quite outstanding. The plant is native to India and China. Medicinal ginger is prepared from the dried "root", condimental ginger from the green. Candied ginger is made from carefully selected, succulent young rhizomes which are washed and peeled and then preserved in jars of syrup.

Choose tubers that are fresh looking and firm. The little new sprouts that appear on the sides of the ginger root have a more delicate flavor than the main part of the root and can be grated and used. May be sliced, shredded or grated, depending on the intended use, as well as enhance the character of meat dishes, vegetable combinations and desserts.

To substitute ginger root for powdered ginger, use 1 tablespoon of grated or shredded fresh ginger root in place of ⅛ teaspoon of powdered ginger. It is low in calories, with 3½ oz. containing only 49, plus a good amount of calcium, phosphorus, iron, potassium and Vitamin A.

GOURDS, Ornamental. These are a result of cross-pollination and have become quite popular in recent years as a colorful adjunct to Thanksgiving and Christmas table and room decorations to herald the coming of fall and winter. Otherwise, no value.

HORSERADISH. Horseradish (German mustard) is grown mainly for its root, which is ground up and mixed with vinegar for a condiment. It has a "hot" taste given to it by its pungent, highly volatile oil.

It belongs to the cabbage, turnip, mustard family, comes to us from Great Britain, where it is thought to have been naturalized from some more Eastern Europe country. It is often found growing wild in moist locations, such as margins of streams, in cool woods, and damp meadows, and in some places, notably in the State of New York, is troublesome as a weed.

Surprisingly enough, raw horseradish, per 100 grams of edible portion, contains 87 calories and a very good amount of calcium, phosphorus and potassium. Prepared horseradish provides only 38 calories per 100 grams, contains less phosphorus and potassium, and more sodium, than raw.

JICAMA (hic-a-ma). A root tuber grown in tropical America and used by Mexican families as the potato is used in the U.S. Said to be a great favorite with travellers, as it quenches thirst and is nutritious. Resembles a turnip in appearance, but has a bland flavor similar to the water chestnut. It is an excellent substitute for the more expensive water chestnut. Choose just as you would a potato; however, the smaller ones are better as the larger ones may be woody. Store in a cool, dry place.

Cut in thin slices, sprinkle with sugar. Two forms recognized: one called agua, with a watery juice, and one called leche, with a milky juice. Cannot be readily distinguished except by tasting the root.

KOHLRABI (coal-rab-ee). This is a member of the cabbage family and a native of Northern Europe. The name is taken directly from the German, meaning, "cabbage turnip".

It has an unusual appearance which distinguishes it from other members of the cabbage family. Instead of a head of closely packed leaves, there is a globular swelling of the stem, some 3 or 4″ in diameter, just above the ground. The leaves are similar to those of a turnip.

Store kohlrabi at 32° F., and 95-98% relative humidity. The young, small globes, not over 3″ in diameter, are the best and have the most delicate flavor. The young leaves of kohlrabi may be cooked like spinach. The globes are best steamed without peeling but may be peeled before cooking. Insert a knife under the tough fiber at the base of the globe and strip off the skin. It is delicious steamed until tender, peeled and cut into Julienne strips. Marinate the strips in French dressing while they are still warm and allow to cool in the marinade. Chill and serve as a salad with cold meat.

Cooked kohlrabi provides only 24 calories per 100 grams of edible portion, and is a fair source of calcium, phosphorus, potassium and Vitamin C. Some Vitamin A and other nutritional elements.

MALANGA. Large herbs of tropical America with thick, tuberous rhizomes, grown in the tropics for the edible roots and sometimes also as greenhouse foliage plants.

MINT. Spearmint and peppermint leaves are both used for flavoring culinary dishes, and should be chosen for their crispness and bright, fresh appearance. A sprig of mint in a cooling drink is most refreshing.

PEAS. These have been used for human food as far back as prehistoric time. In all forms — fresh, canned and frozen — it is still a very major item and National consumption far exceeds the fresh consumption of ten years ago! It is recognized today as a good source of protein, calcium, phosphorus, iron, potassium, thiamine, riboflavin — and a good amount of Vitamins A and C. The greatest nutrient value is found in "fresh".

Originally grown only for their dry seeds, it was not until after the Norman Conquest of England that "green peas" are mentioned in the history of the product. So many fine varieties were developed in England, and, eaten pods and all, they soon became known throughout the World as "English Peas."

Only a small volume is shipped "fresh" annually, about 1,200 cars, with California the principal producer, supplemented by Colorado, Washington and Oregon. When buying fresh peas, get them at their sweetest, most flavorful stage: select fairly large, bright green, angular pods that are well filled and snap readily. A yellowish pod generally indicates over-maturity and, consequently, toughness. Mildew, swollen or highly-specked pods, should also be avoided.

Green peas, like sweet corn, tend to lose part of their sugar content unless they are promptly cooled to near 32° F. shortly after being picked. They will store better in the pod, than shelled, but keep them cold and moist if you *must* store them!

When boiling, use as little water as possible. Drop the peas into boiling water and cook about 15 minutes, or until your sampling indicates "just done". Use onion salt, or cook a small onion with the peas, to add to an already-good flavor. May be served with butter, salt and pepper; creamed, in vegetable salads, soups and stews — or in combination with other dishes.

We have been referring above to the commonly-known green peas. In U.S. markets having a wide variety of fresh fruits and vegetables, there are other varieties:

Sugar Peas. Other names are Sit Dow, Soot Dow and French peas, plus probably the most popular name, "Snow Peas". This is a flat Chinese pea, 3-4" long, about an inch wide, most plentiful from May through September, but available in some supply throughout the year. The pea within the pod is extremely small, with many Oriental dishes including the whole pod in the recipe — the tiny, tender pea within the pod adding a special taste to the crisp pod when eaten.

China Peas. Also known as How Lon Dow, these are slightly smaller in size than sugar peas, and more tender — frequently eaten raw.

Pigeon Peas. Also known as Gandules, these are grown mainly in Puerto Rico and the Dominican Republic, shipped chiefly to the New York area.

Early Dwarf. Many people use this designation for small English Peas, but fresh distribution is practically non-existent. It is actually a variety of English peas.

RAPINI *(ra-peen-ee).* Rapini is a very small turnip plant with no bulb development, which is pulled by hand and marketed with the roots attached. The name is reported to be derived from the Latin name for turnip (rapa) and the suffix (ini), meaning small.

SALSIFY. Member of the Sunflower family, Salsify is sometimes called oyster plant, vegetable oyster and, incorrectly, vegetable marrow. A garden esculent, grown for the fleshy root, which has the flavor of oysters. Very hardy. The seeds (which are really fruits) are sown in early spring. It is easy to grow and it has no serious pests.

It is a vegetable of secondary importance commercially, although it should be in every home garden. Native to Southern Europe, it takes practically a full year to mature and the roots can be left in the ground since they will not freeze. They do become tough in storage and that is why it is suggested they be left in the ground. However, if the storage is cold and moist, can be stored successfully.

Similar in appearance and quality characteristics to parsnips, except that the tops look like heavy grass. Also resembles the parsnip in that its flavor is improved after exposure to cold temperatures.

Values for *raw* salsify range from 13 calories per 100 grams for the freshly harvested vegetable, to 82 calories for the product after storage; corresponding range for *boiled* salsify is from 12 to 70 calories. No sodium content in measurable amount.

SORREL. A member of the buckwheat family, identifiable by its arrow-shaped leaves, and cooked as a green. The name "sorrel" is applied to two distinct types of plants which are used as a food. Both have a relatively high content of oxalic acid, which gives them a sour flavor, but in other respects, are quite different.

The type known as *garden sorrel* is of some commercial importance and closely resembles the common sheep sorrel. The leaves are of a light-dull green color and are narrow and pointed in shape like an arrowhead. Should be bought and handled the same as you would spinach, with which it is usually cooked to add flavor.

The other type is known as *oxalis, wood sorrel, sour grass* or *sour clover*, and is of practically no commercial importance. The leaves are small, light-green and composed of three rounded leaflets resembling those of clover. The stems are upright, tender and vary from light green to red.

Garden sorrel (sheep sorrel) is very low in calories, with 28 calories per 3½ oz. portion, raw, but is extremely high in Vitamin A, Vitamin C, as well as a good content of other vitamins and minerals.

SOYBEANS. Fresh, edible soybeans are seen more and more in the markets and can be distinguished by their fuzzy pods, which are about the same length as those of peas, but much flatter. They generally have a richer flavor than the common beans and are considerably higher in food value. The young soybean sprouts are also used by many people for so-called "Chinese" dishes. The mature soybeans, in their raw state, have a very high Vitamin B_1 analysis . . . and, in addition, are a fair source of Vitamin A, plus a good value of calcium, phosphorus and other elements. Cooked, *immature* seeds contain approximately 118 calories per 100 grams edible portion and provide some Vitamin A and C, calcium, phosphorus. The cooked, *mature* seeds provide approximately 130 calories per 100 grams and are lower in other elements, with no measurable amount of Vitamin C.

SUGAR CANE. From the cane of the same name. Generally packaged in cellophane, 8-10″ sticks. Strip hard cover, chew or shred inner fibrous sugar.

SUNFLOWER SEEDS. The seeds are from the sunflower plant formerly propagated in back yards. In recent years, the seeds have become a snack food, the eater cracking the hull with his fingers, or between his teeth, to secure the tiny, edible kernel. In the organic food movement, the kernels are favored for their heavy protein content and growing of sunflowers has become a very large, commercial venture.

Food composition: hulled, raw sunflower seeds, un-salted, 100 grams (3½ ozs.) edible portion — 602 calories; 26.31 grams of protein, as well as appreciable amounts of fat, ash, calcium, phosphorus, iron, sodium, potassium, thiamine, riboflavin, some niacin and Vitamin A. No measurable amount, if any, of Vitamin C.

TAMARILLO *(tam-a-ree-o)* (Tree tomato). Known in some areas as Cyphomandra. All our research indicates these two items are actually the same; therefore, we are treating them as Tamarillos, since this is the name commonly known in the U. S.

Commercially grown in New Zealand, oval to egg-shaped, about 2″ long with a stem attached. Greenish-purple in color, changing to reddish-purple when ripe. Can be used both as a fruit or vegetable as they combine well with either sweet or savory foods, according to choice. Have good keeping qualities — can be bottled, made into jam, jelly, chutney. Usually used in stews or for preserves; however, can be eaten raw but flavor is subacid. The seeds and skin are usually removed before cooking. To skin, pour boiling water over them to cover; let set for 3-5 minutes and lift out; nick the skin with a knife and skins will slip off readily. To eat them raw, cut in half crosswise and spoon out the pulp, adding sugar for a sweeter dish.

TARO ROOT. Also known as Dasheen, is thought to have come originally from China. It is raised and used mostly in the Southern States, cultivated in many warm regions of the temperate zones such as Egypt, Syria, Japan and New Zealand. The culture of taro has probably reached its highest development in the Hawaiian Islands and it is largely through its extensive use there that the plant has become so widely known among travellers and others. In Hawaii, taro is eaten mostly in the form of poi.

The starch grains in taro are the smallest in any plant, making them readily digestible. The flesh of cooked dasheens ranges from purple or violet to a cream shade. The deep violet-colored "corms", as the tubers are called, are regarded as having a better flavor than the light or cream-colored ones. It can be baked, steamed, boiled or used in soups like potatoes. When buying, the entire tuber should be very firm. Store in refrigerator.

In 100 grams of edible portion of raw taro, there are 98 calories, a good amount of calcium, phosphorus, iron, potassium, Vitamin A, Vitamin G, plus other minerals and vitamins. Extremely nutritious. The leaves and stems are high in ash, calcium, Vitamin C, as well as low in calories.

TARRAGON. Plants may grow to two feet; green, the leaves of which are used for seasoning.

TOMATILLOS *(toe-ma-tee-o)*. Commonly known as ground tomatoes, these little husk-covered green vegetables grow on vines along the ground. They resemble a small green tomato, but taste like a slightly green plum in their raw state. The skin is tough, though thin, like a chili. Quality is good if they are clean and firm, with color from bright green to yellowish green. Husks are always dry. Do not wash until ready to serve. Store in refrigerator.

TOPEPO (tow-pe-po). This vegetable derives its name from the fact that it is a cross between the tomato and Chinese sweet pepper. Topepoes are generally used in salads and should be selected the same way as you would tomatoes.

VEGETABLE MARROW. Should be eaten young, about 1/4 or 1/6 the full-grown size. Member of the squash family. In Europe it is much prized, but in this country, the Crookneck and Scallop types of squash are more popular. Choose and store like squash. A green, cucumber-looking vegetable with thin yellow stripes. Also called Chinese squash (Faahn Gwaah) and "marrow squash".

WATER CHESTNUT. "Chinese water chestnut" and "waternut" are common English names for a tropical sedge, which is widespread in the tropics of the Old World; this species has long been cultivated for its corms, or so-called tubers. These are esteemed as a nutritious delicacy in Chinese cookery and are extensively eaten raw. The skin is chestnut-brown color, has a chestnutty flavor and texture, with white flesh. A plant with the same name is a floating aquatic plant and is considered a pest in some streams in the Eastern United States. Although the corms of this plant can also be eaten, the fruits are quite distinct from the highly edible corms of the Chinese water chestnut.

Corms vary considerably in size; however, in general, only corms of 1-3/16″ or more in diameter are acceptable to the trade. About 60% of the yield is usually marketable, with the smaller corms used for seeding purposes.

Can be successfully stored in a jar, with lid applied *but not airtight* in the refrigerator. If storage temperatures are too high, sprouting of the water chestnuts may occur. May also be stored in plastic bags for short periods, providing the bags are not sealed tight.

Chinese water chestnuts are in greatest demand in the fresh form; however, are also found canned and frozen. Canned water chestnuts lose much of their flavor but retain their crispness, whereas frozen water chestnuts retain the flavor but are less crisp than the canned product.

Crisp, white, applelike flesh that is both sweet and starchy. Flavor similar to fresh coconut. Used best in combinations and seems to blend well with almost any food: omelets, gravies, meat and vegetable stews, soups, mixed salads. When cooked, the texture adds an excel-

lent quality to the dish in which they are used. They are standard ingredients of most Chinese dishes.

Water chestnuts contain calcium, iron and potassium; 100 grams, raw, equal 79 calories.

WINTER MELON. Pumpkin-like melon with a frosty greenish skin, it is most frequently cooked in a pork meat stock to make soup. The Chinese sometimes peel off the rind and quick-cook thin squares for a vegetable dish.

In spite of its name, you will see the winter melon throughout the year; in a Chinese grocery store, you will see the winter melon displayed on the chopping block, where the produce merchant will cut off any size wedge you indicate. They are very large and may weigh 20-30 pounds.

YUCCA (or Yuca) ROOT. Also known as Cassava (or Casava), and applies to any of various tropical American plants of the genus Manihot; especially, M. esculenta, having a large, starchy root. Also called "manioc". The starch derived from the root of this plant is used to make tapioca and as a staple food in the tropics.

NUTS

In the early days of the U.S., very few people bought nuts at the store, for this was a land of many forests and nut trees grew wild. Every fall, the whole family went "nutting", gathering the wild nuts and storing them for winter and spring use. History tells us they gathered beechnuts, hickory nuts, black walnuts, chestnuts and butternuts.

But as time passed, the forests were cut to make way for farms and roads — and these were augmented by towns, cities and highways. While there are still some wild nut trees growing throughout the nation, most of the nuts used today are raised in orchards commercially, in the U.S. or elsewhere.

In general, nut trees grow slowly, but live long. Trees of the walnut, chestnut, pecan and filbert continue to produce nuts a hundred years or more after planting.

Nuts are the dry fruit, or seeds, of some kinds of plants — usually trees. The outside covering of most nuts is the rind or shell. Inside is the softer part of the nut, called by some the "meat" — most in the business prefer calling them the "kernel". Technically, some of the seeds we call nuts are not considered so by botanists. Peanuts belong to the pea family, the almond belongs to the peach family and the cashew is really a part of the fruit of the cashew apple! Nuts are a one-cell fruit.

There are several "mysteries" about the nut business, shared by buyers, merchandisers and consumers. First,

ALFALFA SPROUTS

UGLI FRUIT

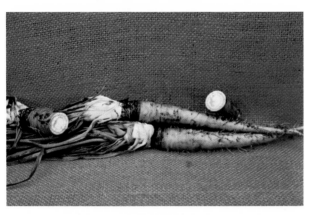

SALSIFY

VERVELOGAS

SOYBEANS (IN SHELL)

YUCCA ROOT (CASSAVA)

SUNFLOWER SEED KERNELS

WATER CHESTNUTS

ALMONDS

PECANS, NATURAL

BRAZIL

PIGNOLIAS

CHESTNUTS

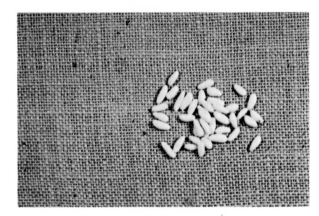

PINENUTS

MACADAMIA

PISTACHIO, NATURAL

U.S.D.A. inspection of in-shell nuts is not mandatory in the U.S., but all nuts are subject to U.S. Food and Drug Administration standards, the latter having authority to seize and condemn nuts found unfit for human consumption. While a packer may not secure U.S.D.A. inspection on his in-shell nuts, if the package contains a U.S. grade marking, he automatically warrants the product to meet that minimum grade of "Extra Fancy", "Fancy" or "Select". Specific requirements of each grade, each variety, are readily available.

Secondly, in mixed nut packages, there is a constant tug-of-war on price, because mixed nuts are a highly seasonal item. A packer, juggling the percentage of the various types placed in the package, can influence the price of the product by as much as 5¢ a pound! While a buyer-merchandiser can secure percentage specifications, it's unlikely a consumer knows enough to demand the "mix" desired at home; we are confident, in the not-too-distant-future, the percentage of pecans and Brazils, possibly other varieties, will be required printing on packages.

Because of different varieties having different densities and sizes, inspection of nuts should be by count and not by weight — whether one is trying to determine mix in mixed nuts or percentage of "cripples". This is in large contrast to most inspection procedures, which are conducted on a weight basis.

"Old Crop" vs. "New Crop": prior to today's modern storage methods, the specifications were important. All in-shell nuts have a natural protection — its own shell! While the biggest damage to nuts is assumption of moisture, in modern storages, modern packaging, it is unlikely "old crop" nuts will be less desirable than the "new crop". Since most nut crops in the U.S. are not harvested and packed prior to November 1-15, it is virtually impossible for retailers to have all "new crop" nuts on display for the first holiday sales.

Nuts-in-shell can be stored by the consumer much more satisfactorily, and longer, than shelled nuts — a very big advantage. There is always the *suspicion* (generally with good reason), nuts-in-shell are lower cost per edible portion. Almost without qualification, home-cracking of nuts to secure whole kernels will be lower cost than the small packages of shelled. As a general guide, one pound of in-shell nuts will produce the following approximate quantity of kernels: English walnuts, 7 ozs.; pecans, 6¾ ozs; black walnuts, 3½ ozs.; filberts, 7 ozs.; almonds, 6½ ozs.; Brazils, 8 ozs.

In the following detailed description of in-shell nuts, we have intentionally avoided our usual advice on "how to select". Most nuts are sold in clear-film bags, or trays with an over-wrap, leaving the consumer very little opportunity to determine quality — until they're in the kitchen. Regardless, as a general guide: the best, initial aid to selection is whether the package contains the U.S.D.A. inspection shield showing U.S. No. 1 (or better) grade. Nuts with clean, bright shells that are not dull, dirty or stained; that are not cracked or broken; shells that are well-shaped — all are indications of good quality kernels within the shell. (Perhaps more important is the *weight* of the individual nut: if heavy for its size, it's likely to contain a good, meaty kernel.) In Western States, in-shell nuts are generally sold bulk — use the above guide to selection of good quality.

ALMONDS. Scientists consider the almond as a stone fruit, much like the peach, but because most of us know and use only the seed (stone) of this fruit, it is generally accepted as a nut.

Total world production of this variety has been on the increase, with the U.S. producing approximately 70,000 short tons, Italy approximately 40,000 and Spain close to that figure. Because of the tremendous world demand for almonds, and the dominant U.S. production, California now exports to almost all European countries, and much of the rest of the world.

Historically, almonds were mentioned as far back as the days of Jacob in the Genesis account; almonds were referred to as the "Greek Nut" by the Romans. While the exact origin is unknown, the almond was brought to California from the Mediterranean area during the establishment of missions by the Spaniards. Almost 100 years later, it was finally discovered that the soil and climate of California was conducive to large, commercial almond production.

Almonds, on the tree, look like small, green peaches; when ripe, the hulls open, revealing the nut inside. There are various varieties, some producing a nut with a bitter taste, grown for the flavoring extract. The sweet varieties are generally confined to fresh consumption and are grown extensively in California.

The almond is ellipsoid in shape with a soft, yellowish-tan shell. The kernels are eaten unprocessed, used in cooking and ground to make almond nut butter. The two principal varieties introduced to California in 1938 for commercial production are the Harpareil and the Jordanolo, both having large nuts, smooth, soft shells.

Shelled, naturally ripe, raw kernels contain 598 calories per 100 grams of edible portion, plus the following: 18.6 gm. protein, 54.2 gm. fat, 19.5 gm. carbohydrate, 3.0 gm. ash, 234 mg. calcium, 504 mg. phosphorus, 4.7 mg. iron, 4 mg. sodium, 773 mg. potassium, .24 mg. thiamine, .92 mg. riboflavin, 3.5 mg. niacin, and a trace of Vitamin C.

BEECHNUTS. The early writers of Greece and Rome referred to eating these nuts, men and animals apparently using the small kernels for food since the very earliest times. The nuts grow inside small, rough burrs about as big as a cherry. Two or more small, three-sided nuts are in each burr. Because they are so small, beechnuts are not easy to harvest, infrequently used as a commercial crop. There are no beechnut orchards in the U.S., but the trees grow wild throughout the Eastern part of the country.

Nutritionally, 100 grams of edible portion provides 568 calories, 19.4 gm. protein, 50.0 gm. fat, 20.3 gm. carbohydrate, 3.7 gm. ash.

BRAZILNUTS: These nuts are grown exclusively in South America in dense forests — growing wild, never cultivated! Trees often grow to a height of 150 feet!

The nuts, as you know them, are really the seeds of the fruit, the round fruit that holds the nuts similar in appearance to a coconut, 4-6 inches in diameter, has a brittle crust and a tough, woody shell on the inside. This "pod" may contain 12-30 — or even more — nuts. When the pods ripen and fall to the ground, the hard shell has to be broken open to free the nuts inside. The closely-packed nuts are three-sided, a size and shape very similar to sections of an orange. Thus, the unusual three-angled shape. The rough shells generally measure 1½-2″ in length. The nut meats (kernels) are white, solid and quite oily. Those not used for eating are broken up and crushed for making oil. Brazilnuts are also called "cream nuts" and "Paranuts".

After the small nuts are extracted from the large pod, it is then necessary for the commercial enterprise to place the small nuts (in shells) in dehydrating ovens until the moisture content has been reduced to 10-12%. After this, the nuts are put through a massive, commercial brushing process to brighten the rough, brown skin — many commercial distributors additionally color the shells with a light-brown dye.

Nutritionally speaking, brazilnuts provide 654 calories per 100 grams, edible portion, 14.3 gm. protein, 66.9 gm. fat, 10.9 gm. carbohydrate, 3.3 gm. ash, 186 mg. calcium, 693 mg. phosphorus, 3.4 mg. iron, 1 mg. sodium, 715 mg. potassium, .96 mg. thiamine, .12 mg. riboflavin, 1.6 mg niacin and a trace of Vitamin A.

CASHEW. This nut is the fruit of a tropical American tree believed to have originated in Brazil, now propagated in practically all hot, humid countries; it is of the same family as the mango and pistachio, is a spreading evergreen which grows to a height of 40 feet. The trees bear clusters of pear-shaped fruit called "cashew apples". The apples are juicy and soft, eaten as a fruit in the countries where they are grown.

The Portuguese introduced the tree to Africa and India and they are now grown in the wild, semi-wild and fully cultivated plantations of tropical nations throughout the world. Total world production is unknown, for many countries do not keep crop statistics, but India, East Africa and Brazil (in that order) are the leading producers, the total estimated at approximately 350-400,000 tons.

The kernel of the cashew nut is protected by a double shell, the cavity between the inner and outer shell being filled by a phenolic oily liquid, known as cashew nut-shell oil, principally used in making phenolic resins, noted for their anti-friction properties and also made into a flexible material that is alkali resistant. But the inner shell and kernel retain a certain amount of this oily liquid and thus must be roasted to dissipate the substance, otherwise the kernel would severely burn the mouth and lips of anyone attempting to bite into a fresh nut. The oily substances decompose by heat and the roasted nut can be eaten without the slightest danger.

The cashew kernel is contained in a soft, thick, cellular shell, is kidney-shaped and about an inch in length. The kernel is of fine texture and has a delicate and distinct flavor.

Traditionally, the procedure after harvesting is to break open the inner shell of the cashew by hand and extract the kernel with the fingers. Until recently, India was practically the sole world supplier of shelled cashews, for Indian women, with half a century of experience, were unexcelled in the tedious and delicate work of cracking open the shells and extracting the kernels gently to obtain the greatest percentage of undamaged kernels. In the early 1960's, as many as 200,000 women were employed in India by the cashew industry for this purpose.

In 1965, after much experimentation and expenditure, an Italian firm installed in three plants in East Africa mechanical equipment able to process tens of thousands of tons annually, thus eliminating the world's dependence upon India.

By weight, the ratio of edible kernel gained from the cashew nut is approximately one pound of kernels from four pounds of nut-in-shell.

In the U.S., culture of the cashew tree is limited to the coasts of Florida, primarily south of Palm Beach. As with most nuts, the U.S. is the principal world consumer, with Russia being a poor second.

Nutritionally, 100 grams edible portion of cashew nuts provide 561 calories, 17.2 gm. protein, 45.7 gm. fat, 29.3 gm. carbohydrate, 2.6 gm. ash, 38 mg. calcium, 373 mg. phosphorus, 3.8 mg. iron, 15 mg. sodium (unsalted), 464 mg. potassium, 100 I.U. Vitamin A, .43 mg. thiamine, .25 mg. riboflavin and 1.8 mg. niacin. For salted nuts, sodium value is approximately 200 mg. per 100 grams.

CHESTNUTS. The chestnut belongs to the same

tree family as the beech, although chestnuts and beech-nuts are very dissimilar. Chestnuts have been called the greatest tree-food crop of the world, for in Southern Europe, China and Japan, chestnuts are widely grown for their food value.

The nuts are eaten fresh, boiled, roasted and made into flour. In some parts of Europe, chestnuts are fed to animals and poultry.

Magnificent chestnut forests once stood in America and were prized by the pioneers, but between 1900 and 1940, a blight destroyed most of the native chestnut trees.

The nuts of the chestnut tree are a beautiful brown color, grow within a green burr covered with bristles. The inside lining of the burr is cream-colored and as smooth as silk. The nut has a thin shell with two or three nuts usually growing in one burr. When the nuts are ripe, the burrs break open and the nuts are easily shelled. They may be eaten without cooking, but most people prefer them hot after roasting.

The Thanksgiving and Christmas turkeys, stuffed with dressing that includes whole, chipped or shredded chestnuts, are traditions with many U.S. families.

Practically all supplies of chestnuts originate in Europe, imported through Eastern ports of the U.S. While distribution throughout the U.S. is wide, greatest consumer interest in this nut is concentrated along the Eastern seaboard.

Nutritionally, fresh chestnuts are low in calories, with 100 grams of edible portion providing only 194 calories, plus 2.9 gm. protein, 1.5 gm. fat, 42.1 gm. carbohydrate, 27 mg. calcium, 88 mg. phosphorus, 1.7 mg. iron, 6 mg. sodium, 454 mg. potassium, .22 mg. thiamine, .22 mg. riboflavin and .6 mg. niacin.

CHINQUAPINS. This is a small chestnut tree, or bush, that bears nuts. Its burrs are like those of the chestnut, but generally only one small nut is contained in each burr. The single nut is shaped somewhat like a child's top. The shell is smooth and glossy and a very dark brown color. The kernel is fine-grained and sweet to the taste. Chinquapins grow East of the Mississippi River and throughout the South. A type of Chinquapin, sometimes called a Golden Chestnut, is grown in the Far West.

HAZELNUTS (Filberts). The nut of the Hazel tree, or shrub, sometimes growing wild in pastures and along fence rows. While these wild bushes have nuts that are good to eat, the production is usually small and the shells very hard. The hazelnut was mentioned in writings as far back as 2838 B.C. and was credited with curing many human ills, as well as being considered excellent for baldness and use as a hair tonic!

Turkey has been exporting hazelnuts for over 500 years and continues to be the world's largest producer of approximately 250,000 short tons. The next largest producer is Italy (97,000) and the U.S., a very small producer with around 8,000 short tons.

In the U.S., these are grown commercially only on the western slopes of the Cascade Mountains in the States of Oregon and Washington, with the former state producing more than 75% of the total tonnage. The hot, humid summers of the Eastern States are too warm for large production in those areas.

Hazelnuts grow in clusters, close to the stem of the tree. The husks are thin, having a leaf-like covering with a fringed outer edge. The arrival of the first frost forces the husks open and generally the nuts fall to the ground. The brown nuts are round or oval, with a flat end showing where they were fastened to the tree. Commercially, removed from the ground, orchard dirt is generally washed from the surface and the nuts are placed in bins where pots of sulphur are ignited under the storage areas, the fumes rising through the mass of nuts and bleaching them to an amber color. The nut meats are sweet and firm.

Nutritionally, hazelnuts contain the following per 100 grams of edible portion: 5.8% water, 634 calories, 12.6 gm. protein, 62.4 gm. fat, 16.7 gm. carbohydrate, 2.5 gm. ash, 209 mg. calcium, 337 mg. phosphorus, 3.4 mg. iron, 2 mg. sodium, 704 mg. potassium, .46 mg. thiamine, .9 mg. niacin and a trace of Vitamin C.

MACADAMIA NUTS. This is the generic and common name for the edible seeds of two closely-related silk-oak trees native to Queensland and New South Wales. Other names for the delicately-flavored, rich kernel are Queensland Nut and Australia Nut. The trees are ornamental in appearance, an evergreen, attaining heights up to 60 feet.

The hard-shelled, shiny-round nuts, covered by thick husks, are produced on racemes 6-8" long. The husks split open and release the nuts when the latter are fully ripe. The kernels, used almost exclusively as dessert nuts, bring high prices in food-specialty markets. Macadamia nuts are seldom sold in-shell, for the shell is about one inch in diameter, about ⅛" thick — very difficult to crack! The flavor of the kernel resembles the Brazil nut, but milder and more delicate. The close-grained, reddish timber of the Macadamia tree is considered of value for cabinet-making. The tree is also known as the Maroochie Nut Tree.

While grown in commercial quantities in the Hawaiian Islands, large orchards have been started in California.

The macadamia contains good amounts of protein, calcium, phosphorus, iron, potassium, thiamine, riboflavin and niacin; 3½ ozs., edible portion, contains 691 calories.

PEANUTS. Botanically, the peanut belongs to the same group of plants as the bean and pea, but it possesses the character of maturing its fruit (nut) beneath the surface of the soil, rather than above ground. Peanuts have the softest shells of any of the nuts. From our research, apparently little world trade is carried on in peanuts.

In the U.S., they are raised throughout the South and Indians were growing peanuts in Virginia before white settlers came to America. The peanut is known under the names of "goober", "goober pea", "ground pea" and "ground nut". To be precise, the peanut is a pea, rather than a nut, the term "nut" having been added because of its flavor and oil. The oil that can be pressed out of crushed peanuts is used as a cooking oil, for making margarine, peanut butter and in other products where vegetable oil is required.

There are two general types: those known as "bunch nuts", and, "vine" or "trailing" nuts. Spanish and Valencia are bunch types, others falling in the other category.

Food value per 100 grams edible portion, raw, without skins, provides 568 calories, 26.3 gm. protein, 48.4 gm. fat, 17.6 gm. carbohydrate, 2.3 gm. ash, 59 mg. calcium, 409 mg. phosphorus, 2.0 mg. iron, 674 mg. potassium, 5 mg. sodium, plus some amounts of thiamine, riboflavin and niacin.

PECANS. Pecan growing is an important business throughout the Southern part of the U.S. and the trees can be grown easily from Southern Indiana and Iowa, southward into Mexico. They are thought to have been discovered by the American Indians, who found them growing wild. They have been grown commercially in good quantities since 1850, and are probably a species of the hickory.

Pecans grow in clusters, their thin husks frequently split when the nuts are ripe. The shell is smooth, light brown in color, round in shape (some varieties) but mostly oval. Direct from the tree, the color of the pecan is a dull but rather light brown, are always polished before placed in commercial sale. Some suppliers dye the shells a color indicative to consumer acceptance in their areas of distribution.

Nutritionally, 100 grams, edible portion, of pecans provide the following: 3.4% water, 687 calories, 9.2 gm. protein, 61.2 gm. fat, 14.6 gm. carbohydrate, 1.6 gm. ash, 73 mg. calcium, 289 mg. phosphorus, 2.4 mg. iron, 603 mg. potassium, 130 I.U. Vitamin A, .86 mg. thiamine, .13 mg. riboflavin, .9 mg. niacin, 2 mg. ascorbic acid and just a trace of sodium.

PILINUTS. These are tropical nuts growing on trees which may attain a height of 65 feet and thrive in the Philippines. There are no established commercial varieties propagated. About 15% of the whole fruit is kernel, which is high in fat (about 75%). The nuts are apparently more digestible than some of the other varieties. The shell is thick and hard. Nutritionally, 100 grams edible portion provide 669 calories, 11.4 gm. protein, 71.1 gm. fat, 8.4 gm. carbohydrate, 2.8 gm. ash, 140 mg. calcium, 554 mg. phosphorus, 3.4 mg. iron, 3 mg. sodium, 489 mg. potassium, 40 I.U. Vitamin A, .88 mg. thiamine, .09 mg. riboflavin, .5 mg. niacin and a trace of Vitamin C.

PINENUTS. These are the edible nuts produced by the nut pine tree, the edible seed borne in the pine cone of certain pine trees. Grown in several countries, it might almost be said it is known by a different name in each of the countries in which it grows. In the U.S., it grows well in the Southwest, where sufficient water is available. Those grown in Italy and France are called *Pinoleas* or *Pignolias*. Those from Mexico and the U.S. are known as *Indian Nuts*, *Pignons* or *Piñons*.

The pinenuts grown in the U.S. are usually small, small as an orange seed, never much bigger than twice that size. In South America, Brazil and Chile, pinenuts grow to as much as two inches in length.

History tells us the Indians of the Northwest gathered pinenuts for food in the early days and many of them continue to gather these sweet-flavored, nutritious nuts.

Nutritionally, food value in 100 grams of edible portion *(pignolias)* provides 552 calories; high in protein, 31.1 gm., as well as the following: 47.4 gm. fat, 11.6 gm. carbohydrate, 4.3 gm. ash and 5.6% water. *Piñon* varieties provide the following: 31.1% water, 635 calories, 13.0 gm. protein, 60.5 gm. fat, 20.5 gm. carbohydrate, 2.9 gm. ash, 12 mg. calcium, 604 mg. phosphorus, 5.2 mg. iron, 30 I.U. Vitamin A, 1.28 mg. thiamine, .23 riboflavin, 4.5 mg. niacin and a trace of Vitamin C.

PISTACHIO. Like almonds, pistachio nuts are the seed of a fruit and are sometimes mistakenly called "green almonds", although they are not the shape nor the color of an almond. The pistachio is the stone or seed of the fruit of the pistachio tree, which is an evergreen that grows in tropical climates, the tree reaching a height of around 30 feet. The red fruit, generally about ½" long, grows in bunches. Inside are the seeds or kernels we call pistachio nuts. The nuts have a double shell, the outside one being red and is removed before the nuts are sent to market. The inside shell is thin, smooth and brittle, may be one of several colors.

The natural color of the shell known to consumers is a grayish-white and may be found in the market with this color, or, more frequently, dyed a red simulating the slight skin over the nut — for eye-appeal. The long, greenish seed is used as flavoring in cooking, candies and ice cream. Through these methods, and the usual hand-eating, Americans gobble up 87% of the world supply — close to 30 million pounds!

Turkey, Iran and Afghanistan are the principal producers of the world supply, very little grown in the U.S.; however, new plantings in Central California, with the relatively new Kerman variety, hold promise for substantial domestic supply in the future.

Foreign-grown supplies are the same nut relished by The Queen of Sheba — and are still harvested and processed essentially the same way — by hand! Since the consumer finds it difficult to crack open a pistachio nut to eat the kernel, foreign processors run the nuts through crude equipment that cracks most of the shells under a stone wheel.

Nutritionally, per 100 grams edible portion, pistachio nuts provide the following: 5.3% water; 594 calories; 19.3 gm. protein; 53.7 gm. fat; 19.0 gm. carbohydrate; 2.7 gm. ash; 131 mg. calcium; 500 mg. phosphorus; 7.3 mg. iron; 972 mg. potassium; 230 I.U. Vitamin A; .67 mg. thiamine; 1.4 mg. niacin; measurable amounts of sodium and riboflavin; no Vitamin C.

WALNUTS. In referring to "walnuts", most people consider the rough-shelled, golden "English" walnut as the entire walnut family; however, the words should include "English walnuts", "black walnuts", "hickory nuts" and "butternuts" — all botanically "walnuts".

Black Walnuts. Very few black walnut trees are raised for commercial use. Most of these trees grow wild, or are planted in parks and yards. They have not gained the popularity of the English walnut since their thick, green husks do not split open easily — and the dark shells of these nuts have numerous rough ridges and do not split into halves, as do English walnuts. The delicious nut meat is difficult to free from the husk. Extremely tasty, high oil content. Nutritionally, 100 grams edible portion of black walnuts contain 628 calories, 20.5 gm. protein, a trace of calcium, 570 mg. phosphorus, 6.0 mg. iron, 300 I.U. Vitamin A; no Vitamin C.

Butternuts. Also known as white walnuts, they have been growing wild in the Northeastern States for many years. Have been commercially produced only since 1938. The commercial production is an open-pollinated seedling of the original wild trees. While some people confuse this type of walnut with the black walnut, there is a vast difference between the two, both in flavor and thickness of the shell.

Butternuts are about ½ inch in diameter, about 2 inches long, sweet flavored, almost smooth shell, thin and easily broken. Many of the varieties found growing wild in the New England States have a sticky, furry, difficult-to-crack husk.

Nutritionally, per 100 grams of edible portion, there are 629 calories, 23.7 gm. protein, 61.2 gm. fat, 8.4 gm. carbohydrate, 2.9 mg. ash and 6.8 mg. iron.

English Walnuts are believed to have originated in ancient Persia and spread to Rome, where they were known as "Jupiter's Acorn". Thus, cultivated for at least 2,000 years, carried all over the world by English trading ships, this particular type of walnut eventually became known as the "English Walnut".

In the 1700's, Spanish missionaries brought walnuts to the State of California, and by the 1800's, the walnut industry was well established. Today, the leading world producer of English walnuts is the U.S., producing approximately 100 million short tons annually, 90% of which is grown in California, supplemented by supplies from Oregon. Other world producers are France, Italy and Mainland China.

The trees grow best when the weather is neither too hot or too cold, the nuts growing in clusters, a husk covering the shell of each nut. As the walnuts ripen, the husks open, the nuts fall to the ground and are mechanically harvested. Those failing to fall to the ground are mechanically-shaken from the tree. If the loosened green hull has not fallen off the walnut, hulling is required by special machines that both hull and wash the nuts as they are brought from the orchards.

The nuts are washed and polished in a water-bleach solution to lighten the color of the shell, dried and sorted according to size: large, medium and babies. Most walnuts are dried by mechanical dehydration, for moisture is the biggest enemy of the nut. Prior to packing, vacuum machines automatically lift out nuts partially filled.

The shell of the English walnut is somewhat rough, a golden-tan color, generally oval in shape, splits easily into halves. Five varieties are grown commercially in the U.S., included under the term "soft shelled", as opposed to the black or hard-shelled walnut. Different varieties are distinguishable only by shape and/or shell structure, some varieties being perfectly round.

Nature provides one of the best protections to quality by giving the walnut the hard, outer shell. It's advisable not to crack walnuts until you are ready to use them. After opening a plastic bag of in-shell walnuts, the remaining supply can best be protected by re-closing the bag and placing in the center of the refrigerator. The kernels of cracked walnuts should be placed in a tightly closed jar in the refrigerator to· protect the quality.

The inside of the kernel is white, clear and clean. If the kernel is rubbery, you can be sure it's past its prime. If the color of the inside kernel is a dingy gray, that means oiliness and possibly rancid kernels. Color of the kernel depends upon the amount of sunshine the walnut receives prior to harvest. The darker kernels merely received more sunshine, and many prefer the darker kernels, for they are generally richer, more flavorful.

The English walnut, nutritionally, per 100 grams edible portion, provides 651 calories, 14.8 gm. protein, 99 mg. calcium, 380 mg. phosphorus, 3.1 mg. iron, 30 I.U. Vitamin A, as well as 2 mg. of Vitamin C.

Hickorynuts. Another kind of walnut, the hickory tree is found growing principally in the Central and Northeastern parts of the U.S. Early settlers to the country found the trees growing in our Eastern woods and throughout the South. Indians gathered and stored the nuts for food before the arrival of settlers. Oblong in shape, compressed on the sides, sharp-pointed at the apex, hickorynuts are smooth and enclosed in a rough husk. When the nuts are ripe, the green husks turn brown, start to open, and both husks and their light-colored nuts drop to the ground.

Despite the lack of large, commercial production, there are several varieties of this nut — the pignut is bitter, but the meat of the shagbark, sometimes called shellbark, is sweet and excellent eating.

Nutritionally, hickorynuts provide 673 calories per 100 grams of edible portion, 13.2 gm. protein, 68.7 gm. fat, 360 mg. phosphorus, 2.4 mg. iron.

BUYING "TIPS"

In general, many fresh commodities must necessarily be shipped in firm condition, such as pears, avocados and tomatoes. Better retailers are conditioning these products to just the stage of ripeness the consumer likes — by the time they arrive at the point of sale.

Where applicable, this booklet will tell you how to determine whether these products are ripe, ready-to-eat. Failing to meet the test, it tells how to ripen.

In general, never cut a fruit or vegetable until it is ready to eat.

Another general rule-of-thumb: never attempt to cause the ripening of a product while under refrigeration. Ripen first, then refrigerate.

Buy mature fruit. A green peach or nectarine, for example, will not ripen but merely soften some and wither. A cantaloupe picked too green will soften but will not be sweet and juicy. Some commodities do not gain sugar after harvest, because they have no reserve starch for conversion to sugar. On the other hand, bananas and pears gain sugar as well as tenderness after harvest.

Handle with care. Fresh fruits and vegetables, because of their perishability, require constant attention to keep their fresh appearance. The less you handle them when purchasing, or in the home, the longer their life. Don't pinch, squeeze or poke them, for bruising leads to damage and damage results in more spoilage for you or your retailer.

The nutrients of greatest importance to the average person, which are found in fresh fruits and vegetables and known to be variable in concentration, are Vitamin A and ascorbic acid. In the tables on the following pages, we have not attempted to burden you with all the variables of many commodities, but the tables do give a good representation of vitamins and minerals found generally in that commodity.

To illustrate the complexity of a completely accurate listing: of the 25 or more apple varieties the average consumer might purchase in a retail store, practically all vary from each other to some extent in ascorbic acid content. For carrot Vitamin A content, three varieties represent practically all U.S. production; all three generally vary considerably — not only by variety but area of production and root maturity. For corn-on-the-cob, carbohydrate content varies by variety and maturity.

Thus, it was felt an easy-to-read, ready reference as a guide, taking into consideration the principal varieties, principal times of purchase, would be more practical. All nutrient contents were secured from U.S.D.A. Handbook No. 8.

You will note the nutrient content tables indicate "edible portion as purchased." Bananas would be a good illustration. If the peel, which is generally not eaten, comprises 32% of the total weight of the product, then only 68% of the banana (as purchased) would be considered an edible portion. For apples, fresh use, generally the peel is eaten, and thus every part of the apple, except stem and core, were considered. You can assume nutrient content of the various products listed in the tables includes only the part or parts of that commodity most individuals in the U.S. would eat.

FOOD AND NUTRITION BOARD, NATIONAL ACADEMY OF SCIENCES–NATIONAL RESEARCH COUNCIL

RECOMMENDED DAILY DIETARY ALLOWANCES,[a] Revised 1968

Designed for the maintenance of good nutrition of practically all healthy people in the U.S.A.

	Age[b] (years) From	Up to	Weight (kg)	(lbs)	Height (cm)	(in.)	kcal	Protein (gm)	Fat-Soluble Vitamins — Vitamin A Activity (IU)	Vitamin D (IU)	Vitamin E Activity (IU)	Water-Soluble Vitamins — Ascorbic Acid (mg)	Folacin[c] (mg)	Niacin (mg equiv)[d]	Riboflavin (mg)	Thiamin (mg)	Vitamin B_6 (mg)	Vitamin B_{12} (µg)	Minerals — Calcium (g)	Phosphorus (g)	Iodine (µg)	Iron (mg)	Magnesium (mg)
Infants	0	1/6	4	9	55	22	kg × 120	kg × 2.2[e]	1,500	400	5	35	0.05	5	0.4	0.2	0.2	1.0	0.4	0.2	25	6	40
	1/6	1/2	7	15	63	25	kg × 110	kg × 2.0[e]	1,500	400	5	35	0.05	7	0.5	0.4	0.3	1.5	0.5	0.4	40	10	60
	1/2	1	9	20	72	28	kg × 100	kg × 1.8[e]	1,500	400	5	35	0.1	8	0.6	0.5	0.4	2.0	0.6	0.5	45	15	70
Children	1	2	12	26	81	32	1,100	25	2,000	400	10	40	0.1	8	0.6	0.6	0.5	2.0	0.7	0.7	55	15	100
	2	3	14	31	91	36	1,250	25	2,000	400	10	40	0.2	8	0.7	0.6	0.6	2.5	0.8	0.8	60	15	150
	3	4	16	35	100	39	1,400	30	2,500	400	10	40	0.2	9	0.8	0.7	0.7	3	0.8	0.8	70	10	200
	4	6	19	42	110	43	1,600	30	2,500	400	10	40	0.2	11	0.9	0.8	0.9	4	0.8	0.8	80	10	200
	6	8	23	51	121	48	2,000	35	3,500	400	15	40	0.2	13	1.1	1.0	1.0	4	0.9	0.9	100	10	250
	8	10	28	62	131	52	2,200	40	3,500	400	15	40	0.3	15	1.2	1.1	1.2	5	1.0	1.0	110	10	250
Males	10	12	35	77	140	55	2,500	45	4,500	400	20	40	0.4	17	1.3	1.3	1.4	5	1.2	1.2	125	10	300
	12	14	43	95	151	59	2,700	50	5,000	400	20	45	0.4	18	1.4	1.4	1.6	5	1.4	1.4	135	18	350
	14	18	59	130	170	67	3,000	60	5,000	400	25	55	0.4	20	1.5	1.5	1.8	5	1.4	1.4	150	18	400
	18	22	67	147	175	69	2,800	60	5,000	400	30	60	0.4	18	1.6	1.4	2.0	5	0.8	0.8	140	10	400
	22	35	70	154	175	69	2,800	65	5,000	—	30	60	0.4	18	1.7	1.4	2.0	5	0.8	0.8	110	10	350
	35	55	70	154	173	68	2,600	65	5,000	—	30	60	0.4	17	1.7	1.3	2.0	5	0.8	0.8	125	10	350
	55	75+	70	154	171	67	2,400	65	5,000	—	30	60	0.4	14	1.7	1.2	2.0	6	0.8	0.8	110	10	350
Females	10	12	35	77	142	56	2,250	50	4,500	400	20	40	0.4	15	1.3	1.1	1.4	5	1.2	1.2	110	18	300
	12	14	44	97	154	61	2,300	50	5,000	400	20	45	0.4	15	1.4	1.2	1.6	5	1.3	1.3	115	18	350
	14	16	52	114	157	62	2,400	55	5,000	400	25	50	0.4	16	1.4	1.2	1.8	5	1.3	1.3	120	18	350
	16	18	54	119	160	63	2,300	55	5,000	400	25	50	0.4	15	1.5	1.2	2.0	5	1.3	1.3	115	18	350
	18	22	58	128	163	64	2,000	55	5,000	400	25	55	0.4	13	1.5	1.0	2.0	5	0.8	0.8	100	18	350
	22	35	58	128	163	64	2,000	55	5,000	—	25	55	0.4	13	1.5	1.0	2.0	5	0.8	0.8	100	18	300
	35	55	58	128	160	63	1,850	55	5,000	—	25	55	0.4	13	1.5	1.0	2.0	5	0.8	0.8	90	18	300
	55	75+	58	128	157	62	1,700	55	5,000	—	25	55	0.4	13	1.5	1.0	2.0	6	0.8	0.8	80	10	300
Pregnancy							+200	65	6,000	400	30	60	0.8	15	1.8	+0.1	2.5	8	+0.4	+0.4	125	18	450
Lactation							+1,000	75	8,000	400	30	60	0.5	20	2.0	+0.5	2.5	6	+0.5	+0.5	150	18	450

[a] The allowance levels are intended to cover individual variations among most normal persons **as they live in the United States under usual environmental stresses. The recommended allowances can be attained with a variety of common foods, providing other nutrients for which human requirements have been less well defined. See text for more-detailed discussion of allowances and of nutrients not tabulated.

[b] Entries on lines for age range 22–35 years represent the reference man and woman at age 22. All other entries represent allowances for the midpoint of the specified age range.

[c] The folacin allowances refer to dietary sources as determined by *Lactobacillus casei* assay. Pure forms of folacin may be effective in doses less than ¼ of the RDA.

[d] Niacin equivalents include dietary sources of the vitamin itself plus 1 mg equivalent for each 60 mg of dietary tryptophan.

[e] Assumes protein equivalent to human milk. For proteins not 100 percent utilized factors should be increased proportionately.

kcal = kilogram calorie : same calorie designation in common usage
gm = gram : 28.350 grams equals one ounce
kg = kilogram : 1,000 grams or 2.2046 pounds
mg = milligram : one-thousandth of a gram
µg = microgram : one-millionth of a gram
IU = international units

COMPOSITION OF FOODS, 100 GRAMS (3½ oz.), EDIBLE PORTION

(Numbers in parentheses denote values imputed—usually from another form of the food or from a similar food. Zero in parentheses indicates that the amount of a constituent probably is none or is too small to measure. Dashes denote lack of reliable data for a constituent believed to be present in measurable amount. Calculated values, as those based on a recipe, are not in parentheses)

Food and description	Water Percent	Food energy Calories	Protein Grams	Fat Grams	Carbohydrate Total Grams	Ash Grams	Calcium Milligrams	Phosphorus Milligrams	Iron Milligrams	Sodium Milligrams	Potassium Milligrams	Vitamin A value International units	Thiamine Milligrams	Riboflavin Milligrams	Niacin Milligrams	Ascorbic acid Milligrams
ALMONDS:																
Dried	4.7	598	18.6	54.2	19.5	3.0	234	504	4.7	4	773	0	.24	.92	3.5	Trace
Roasted and salted	.7	627	18.6	57.7	19.5	3.5	235	504	4.7	198	773	0	.05	.92	3.5	0
APPLES, raw, commercial varieties:																
Freshly harvested and stored:																
Not pared	84.4	58	.2	.6	14.5	.3	7	10	.3	1	110	90	.03	.02	.1	4
Pared	85.1	54	.2	.3	14.1	.3	6	10	.3	1	110	40	.03	.02	.1	2
APRICOTS, raw	85.3	51	1.0	.2	12.8	.7	17	23	.5	1	281	2700	.03	.04	.6	10
ARTICHOKES:																
Globe or French:																
Raw, fresh-harvested	85.5	9	2.9	.2	10.6	.8	51	88	1.3	43	430	160	.08	.05	1.0	12
Cooked, boiled, drained, fresh-harvested	86.5	9	2.8	.2	9.9	.6	51	69	1.1	30	301	150	.07	.04	.7	8
Jerusalem, raw, fresh-harvested	79.8	7	2.3	.1	16.7	1.1	14	78	3.4	-	-	20	.20	.06	1.3	4
ASPARAGUS:																
Raw spears	91.7	26	2.5	.2	5.0	.6	22	62	1.0	2	278	900	.18	.20	1.5	33
Cooked spears, boiled, drained	93.6	20	2.2	.2	3.6	.4	21	50	.6	1	183	900	.16	.18	1.4	26
AVOCADOS, raw:																
California, mainly Fuerte	73.6	171	2.2	17.0	6.0	1.2	10	42	.6	4	604	290	.11	.20	1.6	14
Florida	78.0	128	1.3	11.0	8.8	.9	10	42	.6	4	604	290	.11	.20	1.6	14
BAMBOO SHOOTS	91.0	27	2.6	.3	5.2	.9	13	59	.5	-	533	20	.15	.07	.6	4
BANANAS, raw:																
Common	75.7	85	1.1	.2	22.2	.8	8	26	.7	1	370	190	.05	.06	.7	10
Red	74.4	90	1.2	.2	23.4	.8	10	18	.8	1	370	400	.05	.04	.6	(10)
BEANS, Fava	81	53	5.6	.6	6.6	-	22	95	1.9	50	250	350	.17	.11	1.5	33
BEANS, lima, immature seeds:																
Raw	67.5	123	8.4	.5	22.1	1.5	52	142	2.8	2	650	290	.24	.12	1.4	29
Cooked, boiled, drained	71.1	111	7.6	.5	19.8	1.0	47	121	2.5	1	422	280	.18	.10	1.3	17
BEANS, snap:																
Green:																
Raw	90.1	32	1.9	.2	7.1	.7	56	44	.8	7	243	600	.08	.11	.5	19
Cooked, boiled, drained	92.4	25	1.6	.2	5.4	.4	50	37	.6	4	151	540	.07	.09	.5	12
Yellow or wax:																
Raw	91.4	27	1.7	.2	6.0	.7	56	43	.8	7	243	250	.08	.11	.5	20
Cooked, boiled, drained	93.4	22	1.4	.2	4.6	.4	50	37	.6	3	151	230	.07	.09	.5	13
BEAN SPROUTS, mung:																
Mature seeds, dry, raw	10.7	340	24.2	1.3	60.3	3.5	118	340	7.7	6	1028	80	.38	.21	2.6	-
Sprouted seeds:																
Uncooked	88.8	35	3.8	.2	6.6	.6	19	64	1.3	5	223	20	.13	.13	.8	19
Cooked, boiled, drained	91.0	28	3.2	.2	5.2	.4	17	48	.9	4	156	20	.09	.10	.7	6
BEECHNUTS	6.6	568	19.4	50.0	20.3	3.7	-	-	-	-	-	-	-	-	-	-
BEETS, common, red:																
Raw	87.3	43	1.6	.1	9.9	1.1	16	33	.7	60	335	20	.03	.05	.4	10
Cooked, boiled, drained	90.9	32	1.1	.1	7.2	.7	14	23	.5	43	208	20	.03	.04	.3	6
BEET GREENS, common:																
Raw	90.9	24	2.2	.3	4.6	2.0	119	40	3.3	130	570	6100	.10	.22	.4	30
Cooked, boiled, drained	93.6	18	1.7	.2	3.3	1.2	99	25	1.9	76	332	5100	.07	.15	.3	15
BLACKBERRIES including dewberries, boysenberries and youngberries, raw	84.5	58	1.2	.9	12.9	.5	32	19	.9	1	170	200	.03	.04	.4	21
BLUEBERRIES, raw	83.2	62	.7	.5	15.3	.3	15	13	1.0	1	81	100	(.03)	(.06)	(.5)	14
BRAZILNUTS	4.6	654	14.3	66.9	10.9	3.3	186	693	3.3	1	715	Trace	.96	.12	1.6	-

Food	Water %	Cal	Protein	Fat	Carb	Fiber	Ca	P	Fe	Na	K	A	Thiamin	Ribo	Niacin	C
BROCCOLI:																
Raw spears, cluster and leaves	89.1	32	3.6	.3	5.9	1.1	103	78	1.1	15	382	2500	.10	.23	.9	113
Cooked spears, boiled, drained	91.3	26	3.1	.3	4.5	.8	88	62	.8	10	267	2500	.09	.20	.8	90
BRUSSELS SPROUTS:																
Raw	85.2	45	4.9	.4	8.3	1.2	36	80	1.5	14	390	550	.10	.16	.9	102
Cooked, boiled, drained	88.2	36	4.2	.4	6.4	.8	32	72	1.1	10	273	520	.08	.14	.8	87
BUTTERNUTS	3.8	629	23.7	61.2	8.4	2.9	—	—	6.8	—	—	—	—	—	—	—
CABBAGE:																
Common varieties:																
Raw, fresh-harvested	92.4	24	1.3	.2	5.4	.7	49	29	.7	20	233	130	.05	.05	.3	51
Cooked, boiled until tender, drained:																
Shredded, cooked in small amount of water	93.9	20	1.1	.2	4.3	.5	44	20	.3	14	163	130	.04	.04	.3	33
Wedges, cooked in large amount of water	94.3	18	1.0	.2	4.0	.5	42	17	.3	13	151	120	.02	.02	.1	24
Red, raw	90.2	31	2.0	.2	6.9	.7	42	35	.8	26	268	40	.09	.06	.4	61
Savoy, raw	92.0	24	2.4	.2	4.6	.8	67	54	.9	22	269	200	.05	.08	.3	55
CABBAGE, Chinese (also called celery cabbage or petsai), compact heading type, raw	95.0	14	1.2	.1	3.0	.7	43	40	.6	23	253	150	.05	.04	.6	25
CARAMBOLA, raw	90.4	35	.7	.5	8.0	.4	4	17	1.5	2	192	1200	.04	.02	.3	35
CARDOON	94.0	10	.7	.1	1.8	—	70	23	.7	170	400	120	.02	.03	.3	2
CARROTS:																
Raw, average	88.2	42	1.1	.2	9.7	.8	37	36	.7	47	341	11000	.06	.05	.6	8
Cooked, boiled, drained	91.2	31	.9	.2	7.1	.6	33	31	.6	33	222	10500	.05	.05	.5	6
CASHEW NUTS	5.2	561	17.2	45.7	29.3	2.6	38	373	3.8	15	464	100	.43	.25	1.8	—
CAULIFLOWER:																
Raw	91.0	27	2.7	.2	5.2	.9	25	56	1.1	13	295	60	.11	.10	.7	78
Cooked, boiled, drained	92.8	22	2.3	.2	4.1	.6	21	42	.7	9	206	60	.09	.08	.6	55
CELERIAC, root, raw	88.4	40	1.8	.3	8.5	1.0	43	115	.6	100	300	—	.05	.06	.7	8
CELERY, all, including green and yellow varieties:																
Raw, average	94.1	17	.9	.1	3.9	1.0	39	28	.3	126	341	240	.03	.03	.3	9
Cooked, boiled, drained	95.3	14	.8	.1	3.1	.7	31	22	.2	88	239	230	.02	.03	.3	6
CHARD, SWISS:																
Raw	91.1	25	2.4	.3	4.6	1.6	88	39	3.2	147	550	6500	.06	.17	.5	32
Cooked, boiled, drained	93.7	18	1.8	.2	3.3	1.0	73	24	1.8	86	321	5400	.04	.11	.4	16
CHAYOTE, raw	91.8	28	.6	.1	7.1	.4	13	26	.5	5	102	20	.03	.03	.4	19
CHERIMOYA, raw	73.5	94	1.3	.4	24.0	.8	23	40	.5	—	—	10	.10	.11	1.3	9
CHERRIES, raw:																
Sour, red	83.7	58	1.2	.3	14.3	.5	22	19	.4	2	191	1000	.05	.06	.4	10
Sweet	80.4	70	1.3	.3	17.4	.6	22	19	.4	2	191	110	.05	.06	.4	10
CHESTNUTS:																
Fresh	52.5	194	2.9	1.5	42.1	1.0	27	88	1.7	6	454	—	.22	.22	.6	—
Dried	8.4	377	6.7	4.1	78.6	2.2	52	162	3.3	12	875	—	.32	.38	1.2	—
CHICKPEAS or garbanzos, mature seeds, dry, raw	10.7	360	20.5	4.8	61.0	3.0	150	331	6.9	26	797	50	.31	.15	2.0	—
CHICORY, WITLOOF (also called French or Belgian endive), bleached head (forced), raw	95.1	15	1.0	.1	3.2	.6	18	21	.5	7	182	Trace	—	—	—	—
CHICORY GREENS, raw	92.8	20	1.8	.3	3.8	1.3	86	40	.9	—	420	4000	.06	.10	.5	22
CHIVES, raw	91.3	28	1.8	.3	5.8	.8	69	44	1.7	—	250	5800	.08	.13	.5	56
COCONUT MEAT:																
Fresh	50.9	346	3.5	35.3	9.4	.9	13	95	1.7	23	256	0	.05	.02	.5	3
Dried:																
Unsweetened	3.5	662	7.2	64.9	23.0	1.4	26	187	3.3	—	588	0	.06	.04	.6	0
Sweetened, shredded	3.3	548	3.6	39.1	53.2	.8	16	112	2.0	—	353	0	.04	.03	.4	0
COLLARDS:																
Raw:																
Leaves, without stems	85.3	45	4.8	.8	7.5	1.6	250	82	1.5	—	450	9300	.16	.31	1.7	152
Leaves, including stems	86.9	40	3.6	.7	7.2	1.6	203	63	1.0	43	401	6500	.20	(.31)	(1.7)	92
Cooked, boiled, drained:																
Leaves without stems, cooked in —																
Small amount of water	89.6	33	3.6	.7	5.1	1.0	188	52	.8	—	262	7800	.11	.20	1.2	76
Large amount of water	90.2	31	3.4	.7	4.8	.9	177	48	.8	—	243	7800	.07	.14	1.1	51
Leaves, including stems, cooked in small amount of water	90.8	29	2.7	.6	4.9	1.0	152	39	.6	25	234	5400	.14	.20	1.2	46

COMPOSITION OF FOODS, 100 GRAMS (3½ oz.), EDIBLE PORTION

(Numbers in parentheses denote values imputed--usually from another form of the food or from a similar food. Zero in parentheses indicates that the amount of a constituent probably is none or is too small to measure. Dashes denote lack of reliable data for a constituent believed to be present in measurable amount. Calculated values, as those based on a recipe, are not in parentheses)

Food and description	Water (Percent)	Food energy (Calories)	Protein (Grams)	Fat (Grams)	Carbohydrate Total (Grams)	Ash (Grams)	Calcium (Milligrams)	Phosphorus (Milligrams)	Iron (Milligrams)	Sodium (Milligrams)	Potassium (Milligrams)	Vitamin A value (International units)	Thiamine (Milligrams)	Riboflavin (Milligrams)	Niacin (Milligrams)	Ascorbic acid (Milligrams)
CORN, sweet, yellow:																
Raw	72.7	96	3.5	1.0	22.1	.7	3	111	.7	Trace	280	400	.15	.12	1.7	12
Cooked, boiled, drained:																
Kernels, cut off cob before cooking	76.5	83	3.2	1.0	18.8	.5	3	89	.6	Trace	165	400	.11	.10	1.3	7
Kernels, cooked on cob	74.1	91	3.3	1.0	21.0	.6	3	89	.6	Trace	196	400	.12	.10	1.4	9
CRABAPPLES, raw	81.1	68	.4	.3	17.8	.4	(6)	13	(.3)	(1)	(110)	(40)	(.03)	(.02)	(.1)	8
CRANBERRIES, raw	87.9	46	.4	.7	10.8	.2	14	10	.5	2	82	40	.03	.02	.1	11
CRESS, garden:																
Raw	89.4	32	2.6	.7	5.5	1.8	81	76	1.3	14	606	9300	.08	.26	1.0	69
Cooked, boiled, drained, cooked in -																
Small amount of water, short time	92.5	23	1.9	.6	3.8	1.2	61	48	.8	8	353	7700	.06	.16	.8	34
Large amount of water, long time	92.9	22	1.8	.6	3.6	1.1	58	44	.7	8	328	7000	.04	.15	.7	23
CUCUMBERS, raw:																
Not pared	95.1	15	.9	.1	3.4	.5	25	27	1.1	6	160	250	.03	.04	.2	11
Pared	95.7	14	.6	.1	3.2	.4	17	18	.3	6	160	Trace	.03	.04	.2	11
DAIKON, raw	94.1	19	.9	.1	4.2	.7	35	26	.6	-	180	10	.03	.02	.4	32
DANDELION GREENS:																
Raw	85.6	45	2.7	.7	9.2	1.8	187	66	3.1	76	397	14000	.19	.26	-	35
Cooked, boiled, drained	89.8	33	2.0	.6	6.4	1.2	140	42	1.8	44	232	11700	.13	.16	-	18
DASHEEN:																
Tubers	73.0	98	1.9	.2	23.7	1.2	28	61	1.0	7	514	20	.13	.04	1.1	4
Leaves and stems	87.2	40	3.0	.8	7.4	1.6	76	59	1.0	-	-	-	-	-	2.2	31
DATES, domestic, natural and dry	22.5	274	2.2	.5	72.9	1.9	59	63	3.0	1	648	50	.09	.10	2.2	0
EGGPLANT:																
Raw	92.4	25	1.2	.2	5.6	.6	12	26	.7	2	214	10	.05	.05	.6	5
Cooked, boiled, drained	94.3	19	1.0	.2	4.1	.4	11	21	.6	1	150	10	.05	.04	.5	3
ELDERBERRIES, raw	79.8	72	2.6	(.5)	16.4	.7	38	28	1.6	-	300	600	.07	.06	.5	36
ENDIVE (curly endive and escarole), raw	93.1	20	1.7	.1	4.1	1.0	81	54	1.7	14	294	3300	.07	.14	.5	10
FENNEL, common, leaves, raw	90.0	28	2.8	.4	5.1	1.7	100	51	2.7	-	397	3500	-	.05	.4	31
FIGS, raw	77.5	80	1.2	.3	20.3	.7	35	22	.6	2	194	80	.06	.05	.4	2
GARBANZOS. See Chickpeas.																
GARLIC, cloves, raw	61.3	137	6.2	.2	30.8	1.5	29	202	1.5	19	529	Trace	.25	.08	.5	15
GINGER ROOT, raw	87.0	49	1.4	1.0	9.5	1.1	23	36	2.1	6	264	10	.02	.04	.7	4
GOOSEBERRIES, raw	88.9	39	.8	.2	9.7	.4	18	15	.5	1	155	290	-	-	-	33
GRANADILLA (Passionfruit)	75.1	90	2.2	.7	21.2	.8	13	64	1.6	28	348	700	Trace	.13	1.5	30
GRAPEFRUIT, raw, pulp:																
Pink, red, white (average):																
All varieties	88.4	41	.5	.1	10.6	.4	16	16	.4	1	135	80	.04	.02	.2	38
California and Arizona (Marsh Seedless)	87.5	44	.5	.1	11.5	.4	32	20	.4	1	135	10	.04	.02	.2	40
Florida, all varieties	89.1	38	.5	.1	9.9	.4	15	15	.4	1	135	80	.04	.02	.2	37
Texas, red varieties	87.7	43	.5	.1	11.3	.4	15	15	.4	1	135	440	.04	.02	.2	38
Pink and red (average):																
Seeded (Foster Pink)	88.6	40	.5	.1	10.4	.4	16	16	.4	1	135	440	.04	.02	.2	39
Seedless (including Pink Marsh, Redblush)	88.6	40	.5	.1	10.4	.4	16	16	.4	1	135	440	.04	.02	.2	36
White (average):																
Seeded (Duncan, other varieties)	88.2	41	.5	.1	10.8	.4	16	16	.4	1	135	10	.04	.02	.2	38
Seedless (Marsh Seedless)	88.9	39	.5	.1	10.1	.4	16	16	.4	1	135	10	.04	.02	.2	37
GRAPES, raw:																
American type (slip skin) as Concord, Delaware, Niagara, Catawba and Scuppernong	81.6	69	1.3	1.0	15.7	.4	16	12	.4	3	158	100	(.05)	(.03)	(.3)	4

Food composition data table (values per 100 g; columns left‑to‑right as printed: ascorbic acid, niacin, riboflavin, thiamine, vitamin A, potassium, sodium, iron, phosphorus, calcium, fiber/ash, carbohydrate, fat, protein, food energy, water — food name at right in source).

European type (adherent skin) as Malaga, Muscat, Thompson Seedless, Emperor and Flame Tokay.	4	.3	.03	.05	(100)	173	3	.4	20	12	.4	17.3	.3	.6	67	81.4
GUAVAS, whole, raw:																
Common (average)	242	1.2	.05	.05	280	289	4	.9	42	23	.6	15.0	.6	.8	62	83.0
Strawberry	37	.6	.03	.03	90	(289)	(4)	.9	(42)	(23)	.8	15.8	.6	1.0	65	81.8
HAZELNUTS (Filberts)	Trace	.9	–	.46	–	704	2	3.4	337	209	2.5	16.7	62.4	12.6	634	5.8
HICKORYNUTS	–	–	–	–	–	–	–	2.4	360	Trace	2.0	12.8	68.7	13.2	673	3.3
HORSERADISH:																
Raw	81	–	–	.07	–	564	8	1.4	64	140	2.2	19.7	.3	3.2	87	74.6
Prepared	–	–	–	–	–	290	96	.9	32	61	1.8	9.6	.2	1.3	38	87.1
KALE: / Raw:																
Leaves, without stems, midribs	186	2.1	.26	.16	10000	(378)	(75)	2.7	93	249	1.5	9.0	.8	(6.0)	53	82.7
Leaves, including stems	125	–	–	–	8900	378	75	2.2	73	179	1.5	6.0	.8	4.2	38	87.5
Cooked, boiled, drained: Leaves, without stems, midribs	93	1.6	.18	.10	8300	(221)	(43)	1.6	58	187	.9	6.1	.7	(4.5)	39	87.8
Leaves, including stems	62	–	–	–	7400	221	43	1.2	46	134	.9	4.0	.7	3.2	28	91.2
KIWI FRUIT	56	–	–	.04	–	–	–	–	50	–	–	7.28	.05	.79	36	85.6
KOHLRABI, thickened bulb-like stems:																
Raw	66	.3	.04	.06	20	372	8	.5	51	41	1.0	6.6	.1	2.0	29	90.3
Cooked, boiled, drained	43	.2	.03	.06	20	260	6	.3	41	33	.7	5.3	.1	1.7	24	92.2
KUMQUATS, raw	36	–	.10	.08	600	236	7	.4	23	63	.6	17.1	.1	.9	65	81.3
LEEKS, bulb and lower leaf portion, raw	17	.5	.06	.11	40	347	5	1.1	50	52	.9	11.2	.3	2.2	52	85.4
LEMONS, raw:																
Peeled fruit, summer-shipped	53	.1	.02	.04	20	138	2	.6	16	26	.3	8.2	.3	1.1	27	90.1
Fruit, including peel, pulp	77	.2	.04	.05	30	145	3	.7	15	61	.4	10.7	.3	1.2	20	87.4
LEMON JUICE, raw	46	.1	.01	.03	20	141	1	.2	10	7	–	8.0	.2	.5	25	91.0
LETTUCE, raw:																
Butterhead varieties such as Boston types and Bibb	8	.3	.06	.06	970	264	9	2.0	26	35	.5	2.5	.2	1.2	14	95.1
Cos, or romaine, such as Dark Green and White Paris	18	.4	.08	.05	1900	264	9	1.4	25	68	.7	3.5	.3	1.3	18	94.0
Crisphead varieties such as Iceberg, New York and Great Lakes strains	5	.3	.06	.06	330	175	9	.5	22	20	.5	2.9	.1	.9	13	95.5
Looseleaf, or bunching varieties, such as Grand Rapids, Salad Bowl, Simpson	18	.4	.08	.05	1900	264	9	1.4	25	68	.7	3.5	.3	1.3	18	94.0
LIMA BEANS. See Beans, lima.																
LIMES, acid type, raw	37	.2	.02	.03	10	102	2	.6	18	33	.5	9.5	.2	.7	28	89.3
Canned, solids and liquid	24	(.4)	(.04)	(.03)	(200)	170	(1)	1.2	17	35	.6	14.9	.6	1.0	62	83.0
LOGANBERRIES, raw	24	.4	.04	.03	200	170	1	1.2	17	35	1.6	12.4	.3	1.0	62	86.5
LOQUATS	1	.2	.04	.10	670	348	10	.4	36	20	.5	16.4	.3	.4	48	81.9
LYCHEES: Raw	42	–	–	.34	–	170	3	.5	8	33	.3	16.4	.3	.9	64	81.9
Dried	–	1.3	.11	–	0	1100	3	2.0	33	48	1.2	70.7	1.2	3.8	277	22.3
MACADAMIA NUTS	0	1.1	.34	–	0	264	–	1.7	48	48	2.0	15.9	71.6	7.8	691	3.0
MANDARIN ORANGES. See Tangerines.																
MANGOS, raw	35	1.1	.05	.05	4800	189	7	.4	13	10	.4	16.8	.4	.7	66	81.7
MANGOSTEEN	2	–	–	–	–	–	–	.8	12	–	.8	–	–	.6	63	83.0
MELONS. See Muskmelons.																
MUSHROOMS:																
Agaricus campestris, cultivated commercially: Raw	3	4.2	.46	.10	Trace	414	15	.8	116	6	.8	4.4	.3	2.7	28	90.4
Canned, solids and liquid	2	2.0	.25	.02	Trace	197	400	.5	68	6	.5	2.4	.1	1.9	17	93.1
Other edible species, raw	3	6.8	.33	.10	Trace	375	10	1.4	97	13	1.0	6.5	.6	1.9	35	89.1
MUSKMELONS, raw:																
Cantaloupes, orange flesh	33	.6	.03	.04	3400	251	12	.4	16	14	.3	7.5	.1	.7	30	91.2
Casaba (Golden Beauty)	13	(.6)	(.03)	(.04)	30	(251)	(12)	(.4)	(16)	(14)	.3	6.5	Trace	1.2	27	91.5
Honeydew	23	.6	.03	.04	40	251	12	.4	16	14	.6	7.7	.3	.8	33	90.6
MUSTARD GREENS:																
Raw	97	.8	.22	.11	7000	377	32	3.0	50	183	.8	5.6	.5	3.0	31	89.5
Cooked, boiled, drained	48	.6	.14	.08	5800	220	18	1.8	32	138	.6	4.0	.4	2.2	23	92.6
NECTARINES, raw	13	–	–	–	1650	294	6	.5	24	4	.4	17.1	Trace	.6	64	81.8

COMPOSITION OF FOODS, 100 GRAMS (3½ oz.), EDIBLE PORTION

(Numbers in parantheses denote values imputed—usually from another form of the food or from a similar food. Zero in parentheses indicates that the amount of a constituent probably is none or is too small to measure. Dashes denote lack of reliable data for a constituent believed to be present in measurable amount. Calculated values, as those based on a recipe, are not in parentheses.)

Food and description	Water Percent	Food energy Calories	Protein Grams	Fat Grams	Carbohydrate Total Grams	Ash Grams	Calcium Milligrams	Phosphorus Milligrams	Iron Milligrams	Sodium Milligrams	Potassium Milligrams	Vitamin A value International units	Thiamine Milligrams	Riboflavin Milligrams	Niacin Milligrams	Ascorbic acid Milligrams
NEW ZEALAND SPINACH:																
Raw	92.6	19	2.2	.3	3.1	1.8	58	46	2.6	159	795	4300	.04	.17	.6	30
Cooked, boiled, drained	94.8	13	1.7	.2	2.1	1.2	48	28	1.5	92	463	3600	.03	.10	.5	14
OKRA:																
Raw	88.9	36	2.4	.3	7.6	.8	92	51	.6	3	249	520	(.17)	(.21)	(1.0)	31
Cooked, boiled, drained	91.1	29	2.0	.3	6.0	.6	92	41	.5	2	174	490	(.13)	(.18)	(.9)	20
ONIONS, mature (dry):																
Raw, yellow skin	89.1	38	1.5	.1	8.7	.6	27	36	.5	10	157	40	.03	.04	.2	10
Cooked, boiled, drained, yellow skin	91.8	29	1.2	.1	6.5	.4	24	29	.4	7	110	40	.03	.03	.2	7
Dehydrated, flaked, yellow skin	4.0	350	8.7	1.3	82.1	3.9	166	273	2.9	88	1383	200	.25	.18	1.4	35
ONIONS, young green (bunching varieties), raw:																
Bulb and entire top	89.4	36	1.5	.2	8.2	.7	51	39	1.0	5	231	(2000)	.05	.05	.4	32
Bulb and white portion of top	87.6	45	1.1	.2	10.5	.6	40	39	.6	5	231	Trace	.05	.04	.4	25
Tops only (green portion)	91.8	27	1.6	.4	5.5	.7	56	39	2.2	5	231	4000	.07	.10	.6	51
ORANGES, raw, peeled fruit:																
All commercial varieties (average)	86.0	49	1.0	.2	12.2	.6	41	20	.4	1	200	200	.10	.04	.4	(50)
California:																
Navels (average)	85.4	51	1.3	.1	12.7	.5	40	22	.4	1	194	(200)	.10	.04	.4	(61)
Valencias (average)	85.6	51	1.2	.3	12.4	.5	40	22	.8	1	190	(200)	.10	.04	.4	(49)
Florida:																
All commercial varieties (average)	86.4	47	.7	(.2)	12.0	.7	43	17	.2	1	(206)	(200)	.10	.04	.4	(45)
Fruit, including peel (California Valencias)	82.3	40	1.3	.3	15.5	.6	70	22	.8	2	196	250	.10	.05	.5	71
ORANGE JUICE, raw:																
All commercial varieties (average)	88.3	45	.7	.2	10.4	.4	11	17	.2	1	200	200	.09	.03	.4	50
California:																
Navels (average)	87.2	48	1.0	.1	11.3	.4	11	18	.2	1	194	200	.09	.03	.4	61
Valencias (average)	87.8	47	1.0	.3	10.5	.4	11	19	.3	1	190	200	.09	.03	.4	49
Florida:																
All commercial varieties (average)	88.8	43	.6	.2	10.0	.4	10	16	.2	1	206	200	.09	.03	.4	45
Early and midseason oranges (Hamlin, Parson Brown, Pine-apple) (average)	89.6	40	.5	.2	9.3	.4	10	15	.2	1	208	200	.09	.03	.4	51
Late season (Valencias)(average)	88.3	45	.6	(.2)	10.5	.4	10	18	.2	1	203	200	.09	.03	.4	37
Temple (average)	88.0	54	(.5)	(.2)	12.9	.4	(10)	17	.2	1	–	(200)	.09	.03	.4	50
PAPAWS, common, North American type, raw	76.6	85	5.2	.9	16.8	.5	–	–	–	–	–	1750	–	–	–	–
PAPAYAS, raw	88.7	39	.6	.1	10.0	.6	20	16	.3	3	234	1750	.04	.04	.3	56
PARSLEY, common garden (plain) and curled-leaf varieties, raw	85.1	44	3.6	.6	8.5	2.2	203	63	6.2	45	727	8500	.12	.26	1.2	172
PARSNIPS:																
Raw (year-around average)	79.1	76	1.7	.5	17.5	1.2	50	77	.7	12	541	30	.08	.09	.2	16
Cooked, boiled, drained	82.2	66	1.5	.5	14.9	.9	45	62	.6	8	379	30	.07	.08	.1	10
PEACHES:																
Raw, yellow-flesh	89.1	38	.6	.1	9.7	.5	9	19	.5	1	202	1330	.02	.05	1.0	7
Canned, solids and liquid:																
Water pack, with or without artificial sweetener	91.1	31	.4	.1	8.1	.3	4	13	.3	2	137	450	.01	.03	.6	3
Juice pack	87.2	45	.6	.1	11.6	.5	6	19	.5	2	205	670	.01	.04	.9	4
Sirup pack:																
Light	84.1	58	.4	.1	15.1	.3	4	13	.3	2	133	440	.01	.03	.6	3
Heavy	79.1	78	.4	.1	20.1	.3	4	12	.3	2	130	430	.01	.02	.6	3
Extra heavy	74.1	97	.4	.1	25.1	.3	4	12	.3	2	128	420	.01	.02	.5	3
PEANUTS:																
Raw, with skins	5.6	564	26.0	47.5	18.6	2.3	69	401	2.1	5	674	–	1.14	.13	17.2	0

Raw, without skins	5.4	568	26.3	48.4	17.6	2.3	59	409	2.0	5	674	0	.99	.13	15.8	0
Roasted, with skins	1.8	582	26.2	48.7	20.6	2.7	72	407	2.2	5	701	-	.32	.13	17.1	0
Roasted and salted	1.6	585	26.0	49.8	18.8	3.8	74	401	2.1	418	674	-	.32	.13	17.2	0
PEARS:																
Raw, including skin	83.2	61	.7	.4	15.3	.4	8	11	.3	2	130	20	.02	.04	.1	4
Candied	21.0	303	1.3	.6	75.9	1.2	-	-	-	-	-	-	-	-	-	-
Canned, solids and liquid:																
Water pack, with or without artificial sweetener	91.1	32	.2	.2	8.3	.2	5	7	.2	1	88	Trace	.01	.02	.1	1
Juice pack	87.3	46	.3	.3	11.8	.3	8	11	.3	1	130	Trace	.02	.03	.1	2
Sirup pack:																
Light	83.8	61	.2	.2	15.6	.2	5	7	.2	1	85	Trace	.01	.02	.1	1
Heavy	79.8	76	.2	.2	19.6	.2	5	7	.2	1	84	Trace	.01	.02	.1	1
Extra heavy	75.8	92	.2	.2	23.6	.2	5	7	.2	1	83	Trace	.01	.02	.1	1
PEARS, Prickly pears	88.0	42	.5	.1	10.9	.5	20	28	.3	2	166	60	.01	.03	.4	22
PEAS, Black eye	85.0	40	3.3	.3	6.3	-	32	78	1.7	5	220	634	.37	.06	1.3	38
PEAS, edible-podded:																
Raw	83.3	53	3.4	.2	12.0	1.1	62	90	.7	-	170	(680)	.28	.12	-	21
Cooked, boiled, drained	86.6	43	2.9	.2	9.5	.8	56	76	.5	-	119	(610)	.22	.11	-	14
PEAS, green, immature:																
Raw	78.0	84	6.3	.4	14.4	.9	26	116	1.9	2	316	640	.35	.14	2.9	27
Cooked, boiled, drained	81.5	71	5.4	.4	12.1	.6	23	99	1.8	1	196	540	.28	.11	2.3	20
Frozen:																
Not thawed (average)	80.7	73	5.4	.3	12.8	.8	20	90	2.0	129	150	680	.32	.10	2.0	19
Cooked, boiled, drained	82.1	68	5.1	.3	11.8	.7	19	86	1.9	115	135	600	.27	.09	1.7	13
PECANS	3.4	687	9.2	71.2	14.6	1.6	73	289	2.4	Trace	603	130	.86	.13	.9	2
PEPPERS, chili, raw:																
Green	88.8	37	1.3	.2	9.1	.6	10	25	.7	-	-	770	.09	.06	1.7	235
Red	80.3	65	2.3	.4	15.8	1.2	16	49	1.4	25	564	21600	.10	.2	2.9	369
PEPPERS, sweet, garden varieties:																
Immature, green:																
Raw	93.4	22	1.2	.2	4.8	.4	9	22	.7	13	213	420	.08	.08	.5	128
Cooked:																
Boiled, drained	94.7	18	1.0	.2	3.8	.3	9	16	.5	9	149	420	.06	.07	.5	96
Stuffed with beef and crumbs	63.1	170	13.0	5.5	16.8	1.6	42	121	2.1	314	258	280	.09	.17	2.5	40
Mature, red, raw	90.7	31	1.4	.3	7.1	.5	13	30	.6	-	-	4450	(.08)	(.08)	(.5)	204
PILINUTS	6.3	669	11.4	71.1	8.4	2.8	140	554	3.4	3	489	40	.88	.09	.5	Trace
PINEAPPLE, raw	85.3	52	.4	.2	13.7	.4	17	8	.5	1	146	70	.09	.03	.2	17
PINENUTS:																
Pignolias	5.6	552	31.1	47.4	11.6	4.3	-	-	-	-	-	-	.62	-	-	-
Pinon	3.1	635	13.0	60.5	20.5	2.9	12	604	5.2	-	-	30	1.28	.23	4.5	Trace
PISTACHIO NUTS	5.3	594	19.3	53.7	19.0	2.7	131	500	7.3	-	972	230	.67	-	1.4	0
PLANTAIN, raw, white-flesh	66.4	119	1.1	.4	31.2	.9	7	30	.7	5	385	10	.06	.04	.6	14
PLUMS, raw:																
Damson	81.1	66	.5	Trace	17.8	.6	18	17	.5	2	299	(300)	.08	.03	.5	-
Japanese and hybrid	86.6	48	.5	.2	12.3	.4	12	18	.5	1	170	250	.03	.03	.5	6
Prune-type (Italian, Imperial)	78.7	75	.8	.2	19.7	.6	12	18	.5	1	170	1340	.03	.03	.5	4
POMEGRANATE PULP, raw	82.3	63	.5	.3	16.4	.5	3	8	.3	3	259	Trace	.03	.03	.3	4
POTATOES:																
Raw (year-around average)	79.8	76	2.1	.1	17.1	.9	7	53	.6	3	407	Trace	.10	.04	1.5	20
Cooked:																
Baked in skin, without salt	75.1	93	2.6	.1	21.1	1.1	9	65	.7	4	503	Trace	.10	.04	1.7	20
Boiled in skin, without salt	79.8	76	2.1	.1	17.1	.9	7	53	.6	3	407	Trace	.09	.04	1.5	16
Boiled, pared before cooking, without salt	82.8	65	1.9	.1	14.5	.7	6	42	.5	2	285	Trace	.09	.03	1.2	16
French-fried, without salt	44.7	274	4.3	13.2	36.0	1.8	15	111	1.3	6	853	Trace	.13	.08	3.1	21
Fried from raw	46.9	268	4.0	14.2	32.6	2.3	15	101	1.1	223	775	Trace	.12	.07	2.8	19
Hash-browned after holding overnight	54.2	229	3.1	11.7	29.1	1.9	12	79	.9	288	475	Trace	.08	.05	2.1	9
Mashed, milk added	82.8	65	2.1	.7	13.0	1.4	24	49	.4	301	261	20	.08	.05	1.0	10
Mashed, milk and table fat added	79.8	94	2.1	4.3	12.3	1.5	24	48	.4	331	250	170	.08	.05	1.0	9
Scalloped and au gratin:																

COMPOSITION OF FOODS, 100 GRAMS (3½ oz.), EDIBLE PORTION

(Numbers in parentheses denote values imputed—usually from another form of the food or from a similar food. Zero in parentheses indicates that the amount of a constituent probably is none or is too small to measure. Dashes denote lack of reliable data for a constituent believed to be present in measurable amount. Calculated values, as those based on a recipe, are not in parentheses)

Food and description	Water	Food energy	Protein	Fat	Carbohydrate Total	Ash	Calcium	Phosphorus	Iron	Sodium	Potassium	Vitamin A value	Thiamine	Riboflavin	Niacin	Ascorbic acid
	Percent	Calories	Grams	Grams	Grams	Grams	Milligrams	Milligrams	Milligrams	Milligrams	Milligrams	International units	Milligrams	Milligrams	Milligrams	Milligrams
POTATOES: - Continued																
Cooked: - Continued																
Scalloped and au gratin: - Continued																
With cheese.	71.1	145	5.3	7.9	13.6	2.1	127	122	.5	447	306	320	.06	.12	.9	10
Without cheese.	76.7	104	3.0	3.9	14.7	1.7	54	74	.4	355	327	160	.06	.09	1.0	11
Canned, solids and liquid, without salt.	88.5	44	1.1	.2	9.8	.4	(4)	(30)	(.3)	1	250	Trace	.04	.02	.6	13
Dehydrated mashed:																
Flakes without milk:																
Dry form.	5.2	364	7.2	.6	84.0	3.0	35	(173)	1.7	89	(1600)	Trace	.23	.06	5.4	32
Prepared, water, milk, table fat added.	79.3	93	1.9	3.2	14.5	1.1	31	47	.3	231	286	130	.04	.04	.9	5
Granules without milk:																
Dry form.	7.1	352	8.3	.6	80.4	3.6	44	203	2.4	84		Trace	.16	.11	4.9	19
Prepared, water, milk, table fat added.	78.6	96	2.0	3.6	14.4	1.4	32	52	.5	256	290	110	.04	.05	.7	3
Granules with milk:																
Dry form.	6.3	358	10.9	1.1	77.7	4.0	142	237	3.5	82		60	.19	.30	4.2	16
Prepared, water, table fat added.	81.4	79	2.0	2.2	13.1	1.3	31	44	.6	234	335	90	.03	.05	.8	3
Frozen:																
Diced, for hash-browning:																
Not thawed.	81.0	73	1.2	Trace	17.4	.4	10	30	.7	8	170	Trace	.07	.01	.6	9
Cooked, hash-browned.	56.1	224	2.0	11.5	29.0	1.4	18	50	1.2	299	283	Trace	.07	.02	1.0	8
French-fried:																
Not thawed, without salt.	63.5	170	2.8	6.5	26.1	1.1	7	67	1.4	3	506	Trace	.14	.02	2.1	20
Heated, without salt.	52.9	220	3.6	8.4	33.7	1.4	9	86	1.8	4	652	Trace	.14	.02	2.6	21
Mashed:																
Not thawed.	80.4	75	1.7	.1	17.1	.7	16	39	.7	79	229	30	.07	.03	.8	6
Heated.	78.3	93	1.8	2.8	15.7	1.4	25	42	.6	359	215	140	.06	.04	.7	4
POTATO CHIPS (See note).	1.8	568	5.3	39.8	50.0	3.1	40	139	1.8	Vary	1130	Trace	.21	.07	4.8	16
PUMPKIN, raw.	91.6	26	1.0	.1	6.5	.8	21	44	.8	1	340	1600	.05	.11	.6	9
QUINCE, raw.	83.8	57	.4	.1	15.3	.4	11	17	.7	4	197	40	.02	.03	.2	15
RADISHES, raw, common.	94.5	17	1.0	.1	3.6	.8	30	31	1.0	18	322	10	.03	.03	.3	26
RASPBERRIES, raw:																
Black.	80.8	73	1.5	1.4	15.7	.6	30	22	.9	1	199	Trace	(.03)	(.09)	(.9)	18
Red.	84.2	57	1.2	.5	13.6	.5	22	22	.9	1	168	130	.03	.09	.9	25
RHUBARB:																
Raw.	94.8	16	.6	.1	3.7	.8	96	18	.8	2	251	100	(.03)	(.07)	(.3)	9
Cooked, added sugar.	62.8	141	.5	.1	36.0	.6	78	15	.6	2	203	80	(.02)	(.05)	(.3)	6
RUTABAGAS:																
Raw.	87.0	46	1.1	.1	11.0	.8	66	39	.4	5	239	580	.07	.07	1.1	43
Cooked, boiled, drained.	90.2	35	.9	.1	8.2	.6	59	31	.3	4	167	550	.06	.06	.8	26
SALSIFY:																
Raw, fresh-harvested.	77.6	18	2.9	.6	18.0	.9	47	66	1.5	-	380	10	.04	.04	.3	11
Cooked, boiled, drained.	81.0	18	2.6	.6	15.1	.7	42	53	1.3	-	266	10	.03	.04	.2	7
SHALLOTS, raw.	79.8	72	2.5	.1	16.8	.8	37	60	1.2	12	334	Trace	.06	.02	.2	8
SORREL:																
Raw.	90.9	28	2.1	.3	5.6	1.1	66	41	1.6	5	338	12900	.09	.22	.5	119
Cooked.	93.6	19	1.6	.2	3.9	.7	55	26	.9	3	198	10800	.06	.13	.4	54
SOYBEANS:																
Immature seeds:																
Raw.	69.2	134	10.9	5.1	13.2	1.6	67	225	2.8	-	-	690	.44	.16	1.4	29
Cooked, boiled, drained.	73.8	118	9.8	5.1	10.1	1.2	60	191	2.5	-	-	660	.31	.13	1.2	17

Composition of foods — values per 100 grams, edible portion. (Column headings do not appear on this page; values are listed in their printed left-to-right order: Water %, Food energy (cal.), Protein (g), Fat (g), Carbohydrate (g), Fiber (g), Calcium (mg), Phosphorus (mg), Iron (mg), Sodium (mg), Potassium (mg), Vitamin A (I.U.), Thiamine (mg), Riboflavin (mg), Niacin (mg), Ascorbic acid (mg).)

Item	Water	Food energy	Protein	Fat	Carbohydrate	Fiber	Calcium	Phosphorus	Iron	Sodium	Potassium	Vit. A	Thiamine	Riboflavin	Niacin	Ascorbic acid
...ure seeds, dry:																
Raw	10.0	403	34.1	17.7	33.5	4.7	226	554	8.4	5	1677	80	1.10	.31	2.2	—
Cooked	71.0	130	11.0	5.7	10.8	1.5	73	179	2.7	2	540	30	.21	.09	.6	0
SPINACH:																
Raw	90.7	26	3.2	.3	4.3	1.5	93	51	3.1	71	470	8100	.10	.20	.6	51
Cooked, boiled, drained	92.0	23	3.0	.3	3.6	1.1	93	38	2.2	50	324	8100	.07	.14	.5	28
SQUASH:																
Summer:																
All varieties:																
Raw	94.0	19	1.1	.1	4.2	.6	28	29	.4	1	202	410	.05	.09	1.0	22
Cooked, boiled, drained	95.5	14	.9	.1	3.1	.4	25	25	.4	1	141	390	.05	.08	.8	10
Crookneck and Straightneck, Yellow:																
Raw	93.7	20	1.2	.2	4.3	.6	28	29	.4	1	202	460	.05	.09	1.0	25
Cooked, boiled, drained	95.3	15	1.0	.2	3.1	.4	25	25	.4	1	141	440	.05	.08	.8	11
Scallop varieties, white and pale green:																
Raw	93.3	21	.9	.1	5.1	.6	28	29	.4	1	202	190	.05	.09	1.0	18
Cooked, boiled, drained	95.0	16	.7	.1	3.8	.4	25	25	.4	1	141	180	.05	.08	.8	8
Zucchini and Cocozelle (Italian marrow type), green:																
Raw, including skin	94.6	17	1.2	.1	3.6	.5	28	29	.4	1	202	320	.05	.09	1.0	19
Cooked, boiled, drained, including skin	96.0	12	1.0	.1	2.5	.4	25	25	.4	1	141	300	.05	.08	.8	9
Winter (all fresh-harvested):																
All varieties:																
Raw	85.1	50	1.4	.3	12.4	.8	22	38	.6	1	369	3700	.05	.11	.6	13
Cooked:																
Baked	81.4	63	1.8	.4	15.4	1.0	28	48	.8	1	461	4200	.05	.13	.7	13
Boiled, mashed	88.8	38	1.1	.3	9.2	.6	20	32	.5	1	258	3500	.04	.10	.4	8
Acorn:																
Raw	86.3	44	1.5	.1	11.2	.9	31	23	.9	1	384	1200	.05	.11	.6	14
Cooked:																
Baked	82.9	55	1.9	.1	14.0	1.1	39	29	1.1	1	480	1400	.05	.13	.7	13
Boiled, mashed	89.7	34	1.2	.1	8.4	.6	28	20	.8	1	269	1100	.04	.10	.4	8
Butternut:																
Raw	83.7	54	1.4	.1	14.0	.8	32	58	.8	1	487	5700	.05	.11	.6	9
Cooked:																
Baked	79.6	68	1.8	.1	17.5	1.0	40	72	1.0	1	609	6400	.05	.13	.7	8
Boiled, mashed	87.8	41	1.1	.1	10.4	.6	29	49	.7	1	341	5400	.04	.10	.4	5
Hubbard:																
Raw	88.1	39	1.4	.3	9.4	.8	19	31	.6	1	217	4300	.05	.11	.6	11
Cooked:																
Baked	85.1	50	1.8	.4	11.7	1.0	24	39	.8	1	271	4800	.05	.13	.7	10
Boiled, mashed	91.1	30	1.1	.3	6.9	.6	17	26	.5	1	152	4100	.04	.10	.4	6
STRAWBERRIES:																
Raw	89.9	37	.7	.5	8.4	.5	21	21	1.0	1	164	60	.03	.07	.6	59
Canned, solids and liquid:																
Water pack, with or without artificial sweetener	93.7	22	.4	.1	5.6	.2	14	14	.7	1	111	40	.01	.03	.4	20
Frozen, sweetened, not thawed:																
Sliced	71.3	109	.5	.2	27.8	.2	14	17	.7	1	112	30	.02	.06	.5	53
Whole	75.7	92	.4	.2	23.5	.2	13	16	.6	1	104	30	.02	.06	.5	55
SUNFLOWER SEED KERNELS, dry	4.8	560	24.0	47.3	19.9	4.0	120	837	7.1	30	920	50	1.96	.23	5.4	—
SWEETPOTATOES:																
Raw, all commercial varieties	70.6	114	1.7	.4	26.3	1.0	32	47	.7	10	243	8800	.10	.06	.6	21
Cooked, all:																
Baked in skin	63.7	141	2.1	.5	32.5	1.2	40	58	.9	12	300	8100	.09	.07	.7	22
Boiled in skin	70.6	114	1.7	.4	26.3	1.0	32	47	.7	10	243	7900	.09	.06	.6	17
Candied	60.0	168	1.3	3.3	34.2	1.2	37	43	.9	42	190	6300	.06	.04	.4	10
Canned:																
Liquid pack, solids and liquid:																
Regular pack in sirup	70.7	114	1.0	.2	27.5	.6	13	29	.7	48	(120)	5000	.03	.03	.6	8
Special dietary pack, without added sugar and salt	88.0	46	.7	.1	10.8	.4	13	29	.7	12	120	5000	.03	.03	.6	8
Vacuum or solid pack, non-dietetic	71.9	108	2.0	.2	24.9	1.0	25	41	.8	48	200	7800	.05	.04	.6	14

COMPOSITION OF FOODS, 100 GRAMS (3½ oz.), EDIBLE PORTION

(Numbers in parentheses denote values imputed—usually from another form of the food or from a similar food. Zero in parentheses indicates that the amount of a constituent probably is none or is too small to measure. Dashes denote lack of reliable data for a constituent believed to be present in measurable amount. Calculated values, as those based on a recipe, are not in parentheses)

Food and description	Water (Percent)	Food energy (Calories)	Protein (Grams)	Fat (Grams)	Carbohydrate Total (Grams)	Ash (Grams)	Calcium (Milligrams)	Phosphorus (Milligrams)	Iron (Milligrams)	Sodium (Milligrams)	Potassium (Milligrams)	Vitamin A value (International units)	Thiamine (Milligrams)	Riboflavin (Milligrams)	Niacin (Milligrams)	Ascorbic acid (Milligrams)
TAMARINDS, raw	31.4	239	2.8	.6	62.5	2.7	74	113	2.8	51	781	30	.34	.14	1.2	2
TOMATILLOS	91.0	25	1.4	.5	4.2	-	8	34	.03	-	-	380	.15	.03	3.5	4
TOMATOES, green, raw	93.0	24	1.2	.2	5.1	.5	13	27	.5	3	244	270	.06	.04	.5	20
TOMATOES, ripe:																
Raw (year-around average)	93.5	22	1.1	.2	4.7	.5	13	27	.5	3	244	900	.06	.04	.7	23
Cooked, boiled	92.4	26	1.3	.2	5.5	.6	15	32	.6	4	287	1000	.07	.05	.8	24
TURNIPS:																
Raw	91.5	30	1.0	.2	6.6	.7	39	30	.5	49	268	Trace	.04	.07	.6	36
Cooked, boiled, drained	93.6	23	.8	.2	4.9	.5	35	24	.4	34	188	Trace	.04	.05	.3	22
TURNIP GREENS, leaves, including stems:																
Raw	90.3	28	3.0	.3	5.0	1.4	246	58	1.8	-	-	7600	(.21)	(.39)	(.8)	139
Cooked, boiled, drained, cooked in -																
Small amount of water, short time	93.2	20	2.2	.2	3.6	.8	184	37	1.1	-	-	6300	.15	.24	.6	69
Large amount of water, long time	93.5	19	2.2	.2	3.3	.8	174	34	1.0	-	-	5700	.10	.23	.5	47
WALNUTS:																
Black	3.1	628	20.5	59.3	14.8	2.3	Trace	570	6.0	3	460	300	.22	.11	.7	-
English	3.5	651	14.8	64.0	15.8	1.9	99	380	3.1	2	450	30	.33	.13	.9	2
WATERCHESTNUT, Chinese (matai, waternut), raw	78.3	79	1.4	.3	19.0	1.1	4	65	.6	20	500	0	.14	.20	1.0	4
WATERCRESS, leaves including stems, raw	93.3	19	2.2	.3	3.0	1.2	151	54	1.7	52	282	4900	.08	.16	.9	79
WATERMELON, raw	92.6	26	.5	.2	6.4	.3	7	10	.5	1	100	590	.03	.03	.2	7
YAM, tuber, raw	73.5	101	2.1	.2	23.2	1.0	20	69	.6	-	600	Trace	.10	.04	.5	9

Artichokes: for stored product, values are as much as 47 calories, raw, and 44 calories for boiled.

Broccoli: the Vitamin A content for leaves is 16,000 I.U.; for the flower cluster, 3,000 and for the stalks, 400 I.U.

Cabbage: for raw storage cabbage, ascorbic acid value is 42 mg.

Corn, sweet: Vitamin A content of all white corn is a mere trace.

Grapefruit: ascorbic acid content may vary slightly, depending upon time of shipment during the varietal season for marketing fresh fruit.

Onions: Vitamin A content of white-fleshed varieties is only a trace.

Oranges: ascorbic acid content may vary slightly, depending upon time of shipment during the varietal season for marketing fresh fruit.

Parsnips: ascorbic acid value in the fall, within 3 months of harvest, is about 24 mg., drops to less than half of this value if storage exceeds 6 months.

Peaches: Vitamin A value for white-fleshed varieties is about 50 I.U.

Plantain: for deep-yellow flesh varieties, Vitamin A content averages 1,200 I.U.

Potatoes: fresh, recently dug varieties, average 26 mg. ascorbic acid; after 3 month's storage, the value is only half as high; after 6 month's, the average is only one-third as high. For canned potatoes, Federal standards provide for addition of certain calcium salts as firming agents; if used, these salts may add calcium not to exceed 200 mg. per 100 grams of finished product. Values listed for dehydrated potatoes (flakes and granules, with and without milk), will vary in ascorbic acid value considerably, dependent on content of raw potatoes, method of processing, length of storage of dehydrated product. Values of dehydrated forms may range from 20 to 35 mg. ascorbic acid per 100 grams. For frozen, mashed, heated potatoes, sodium content is variable and may be as high as 1000 mg. per 100 grams.